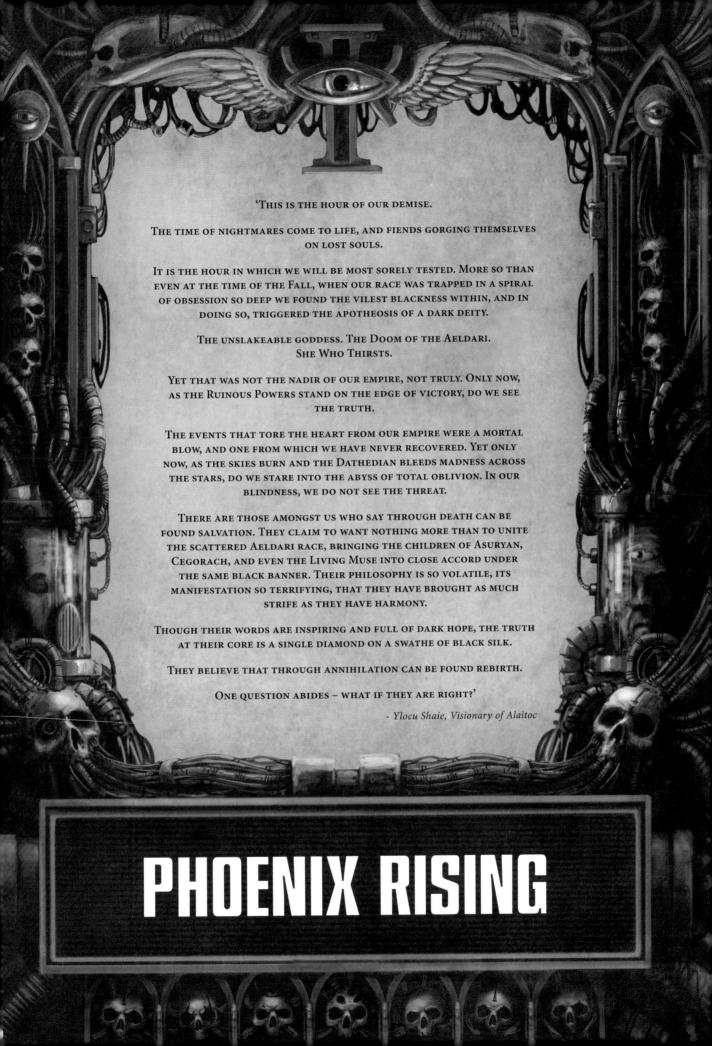

'THIS IS THE HOUR OF OUR DEMISE.

THE TIME OF NIGHTMARES COME TO LIFE, AND FIENDS GORGING THEMSELVES
ON LOST SOULS.

IT IS THE HOUR IN WHICH WE WILL BE MOST SORELY TESTED. MORE SO THAN
EVEN AT THE TIME OF THE FALL, WHEN OUR RACE WAS TRAPPED IN A SPIRAL
OF OBSESSION SO DEEP WE FOUND THE VILEST BLACKNESS WITHIN, AND IN
DOING SO, TRIGGERED THE APOTHEOSIS OF A DARK DEITY.

THE UNSLAKEABLE GODDESS. THE DOOM OF THE AELDARI.
SHE WHO THIRSTS.

YET THAT WAS NOT THE NADIR OF OUR EMPIRE, NOT TRULY. ONLY NOW,
AS THE RUINOUS POWERS STAND ON THE EDGE OF VICTORY, DO WE SEE
THE TRUTH.

THE EVENTS THAT TORE THE HEART FROM OUR EMPIRE WERE A MORTAL
BLOW, AND ONE FROM WHICH WE HAVE NEVER RECOVERED. YET ONLY
NOW, AS THE SKIES BURN AND THE DATHEDIAN BLEEDS MADNESS ACROSS
THE STARS, DO WE STARE INTO THE ABYSS OF TOTAL OBLIVION. IN OUR
BLINDNESS, WE DO NOT SEE THE THREAT.

THERE ARE THOSE AMONGST US WHO SAY THROUGH DEATH CAN BE
FOUND SALVATION. THEY CLAIM TO WANT NOTHING MORE THAN TO UNITE
THE SCATTERED AELDARI RACE, BRINGING THE CHILDREN OF ASURYAN,
CEGORACH, AND EVEN THE LIVING MUSE INTO CLOSE ACCORD UNDER
THE SAME BLACK BANNER. THEIR PHILOSOPHY IS SO VOLATILE, ITS
MANIFESTATION SO TERRIFYING, THAT THEY HAVE BROUGHT AS MUCH
STRIFE AS THEY HAVE HARMONY.

THOUGH THEIR WORDS ARE INSPIRING AND FULL OF DARK HOPE, THE TRUTH
AT THEIR CORE IS A SINGLE DIAMOND ON A SWATHE OF BLACK SILK.

THEY BELIEVE THAT THROUGH ANNIHILATION CAN BE FOUND REBIRTH.

ONE QUESTION ABIDES – WHAT IF THEY ARE RIGHT?'

- Ylocu Shaie, Visionary of Alaitoc

PHOENIX RISING

CONTENTS

PRODUCED BY GAMES WORKSHOP IN NOTTINGHAM

With thanks to the Mournival and the Infinity Circuit for their additional playtesting services

INTRODUCTION

The Aeldari are a race fractured and upon the edge of extinction, yet still the remnants of its once glorious civilisation stand proud and defiant against their many enemies. Their story is one of tragedy and despair, but also hope, for amongst their dwindling numbers are some who preach that salvation can be found through death.

The immense warp storm known as the Cicatrix Maledictum has torn the galaxy asunder. Mankind's realm has been divided, many of its worlds isolated, yet it is not just Humanity that has suffered beneath the Great Rift's baleful light. The Aeldari, a gifted and ancient race who once ruled the stars, have found their struggle for survival brought to crisis point by the psychic energies that abound.

No matter the methods by which they evade their nemesis Slaanesh – that terrible entity born from their own hubris and excesses in aeons past – the Aeldari way of life has been shattered by the influx of Chaos that has set so much of the galaxy ablaze. Now they are tested as never before, forced to take drastic measures in order to ensure their own survival.

Into this uncertain and harrowing era come the Ynnari, scions of the slumbering death god Ynnead. They believe their race can ultimately defeat Slaanesh and even reclaim the cycle of reincarnation that typified ages past. Yet to do so, they must claim the Croneswords of Morai-Heg or, failing that, give their souls to the Whispering God until he has strength enough to set right the dire repercussions of the Fall – and to do that, every Aeldari must die.

Division is sown everywhere these Ynnari tread, for they claim this great risk is the only way their race can ultimately be free and rise victorious from the ashes of defeat. Be they Asuryani, Harlequin, or even Drukhari, there are those who believe they might be right, and that it is always darkest before the dawn.

IN THIS BOOK

This book is part of Psychic Awakening, an ongoing series set in the aftermath of the Great Rift. It covers the perspective of the Asuryani, Drukhari and Harlequins, as well as the Ynnari drawn from across the Aeldari factions.

Inside you will find:

- The unfolding drama of the Aeldari's struggle for survival in the era of the Great Rift.
- Theatres of war and missions to echo the story of Phoenix Rising.
- Additional rules for Craftworlds and Drukhari armies that complement the codexes.
- A suite of rules for the Ynnari designed to supplement *Codex: Craftworlds*, *Codex: Drukhari* and *Codex: Harlequins*, including datasheets for Yvraine, the Visarch and the Yncarne.

THE DATHEDIAN

Towards the end of the 41st Millennium, the galaxy was all but split in half by the Great Rift. To the Aeldari it was known as the Dathedian, and as a highly psychically attuned race, the aetheric phenomena that accompanied it affected them most of all.

The Cicatrix Maledictum, that great tear across the fabric of time and space, has further divided the fractious Aeldari race. After the coming of that celestial cataclysm, the Aeldari craftworlds sent out psychic communiques, reaching out to one another across the void. Two of the world-ships did not respond, their spiritual traces dwindling with every passing hour. Some amongst the Spiritseers of the Asuryani believe their souls have empowered Ynnead, and that the craftworlders will never be seen again.

To an empire as large as the Imperium, this would have been considered acceptable losses, for Mankind's realm contains a million worlds and more. For the Asuryani it was a cost so high it wrenched at the heart. Perhaps one day the lost craftworlds would return, just as Altansar was drawn from the gullet of the warp by the odyssey of the Phoenix Lord Maugan Ra. But for now, they were gone.

Far from uniting the survivors against the tide of Chaos spilling into the galaxy, that great loss fomented discord, and the rift between the factions of the Aeldari grew all the wider. Simple geography was itself a contributing factor, for the craftworlds were too far scattered across the galaxy to easily unite, and even the Aeldari paths through the webway – that maze of metaphysical pathways that spanned the interstice between realspace and the warp – were now battered and torn at by the raging fury of the empyrean. Though the Harlequins continued to walk that strange un-realm at will and do what they could to unite the Asuryani and Commorrite Drukhari in purpose, the resentment and isolationism that had long characterised the fractured Aeldari race worsened.

In the cultural hearts of the Aeldari peoples, the wound of the Dathedian festered in silence. No civilisation could look upon a sky mauled by the warp-stuff of Chaos and not feel affected by it. To a race as sensitive to psychic energies as the Aeldari, the scar in reality was a constant dull ache in the mind, a reminder of all they had lost. Perhaps it would never have existed at all were it not for the formation of the Eye of Terror, born from the sickening cataclysm of Slaanesh's birth. Across the galaxy, nightmares of guilt, doubt and surging aggression wracked Aeldari and Drukhari alike, and they steeped themselves in battle against tides of Chaos-worshippers in the hopes of assuaging these negative emotions.

A new era of war began as the turmoil within was turned into merciless strikes against ancient enemies, emerging foes and former allies. Much of the blame for the disastrous events was put at the door of the rapidly growing Ynnari movement and, by association, upon Biel-Tan. There, the populace had been divided between fervent support for Yvraine, the leader of the Ynnari, and the outright condemnation that followed her visitation – coinciding as it did with the subsequent invasion of the craftworld by a ravening Slaaneshi horde and the fracturing of its infinity circuit. Amidst that appalling catastrophe a new strand of fate was revealed, one that some believed would lead the Aeldari race to greatness once more. The being that Yvraine summoned from within Biel-Tan's broken wraithbone skeleton was an avatar, of a sort, and its very existence was proof of Ynnead having stirred from his slumber. There was a chance that the Whispering God could save their souls from She Who Thirsts once and for all.

A PSYCHE INFLAMED

Barring only those dark kin of Commorragh whose powers have atrophied, all Aeldari possess some

> '*The Aeldari psyche is a powerful weapon. It can slay a distant foe with a pulse of thought. Like any other, it must be used with skill. Since the coming of the Dathedian its edges grow sharper than ever before, its grip more perilous to grasp. The slightest misstep can see its wielder, and even the reality in which they stand, laid open and bloody.*'
>
> – Eldrad Ulthran

degree of psychic ability. Since the Great Rift split the galaxy, those gifts have burgeoned in a variety of different ways.

It is generally accepted amongst the Farseers of the craftworlds that this is a direct result of the Dathedian introducing a vast bleed of aetheric energy into the galaxy. Of all the Aeldari, the craftworlders are most in tune with matters psychic, and without the Path system – that cultural process by which an Asuryani focuses his or her mind upon a single pursuit or skill to avoid the temptation of all others – they may have found this flare of psychic activity maddening, and possibly even disastrous. Yet the discipline of the Path was developed precisely to turn the Aeldari mind into a fortress against such unfettered activity. Of all the civilisations in the galaxy, the Asuryani could be said to have

ridden out the swell of psychic energy the best, for in many ways they had been ready for it. Their entire culture was built around discipline, guardianship and self-denial, to prevent their worst excesses rising to doom them all.

Those Asuryani who trod the Witch Path found their prophetic glimpses escalating into full and potent visions, magnifying their ability to parse the skeins of fate and react accordingly. On every craftworld their Runes of Warding burned out at a daunting rate, the protective symbols being used up almost as fast as they could be regrown from psycho-reactive material. But for now at least, the inner psychic threat posed by their daemonic nemeses was held at bay.

With this influx of psychic energy came other new abilities for the Asuryani. Even those warlike souls

who honed their physical skills over the mental found their talents blossoming when they brought the two into perfect balance. Aspect Warriors channelled the echoes of the war god Khaine and focused the resultant energies through the lenses of their glorious Exarch leaders. When Howling Banshees charged en masse, the wind itself screamed its fury alongside them; when Striking Scorpions gathered in the shadowed recesses of the battlefield, they became all but invisible to the naked eye until they leapt from cover and fell upon the foe. Always the Asuryani had possessed such powers and employed them in battle, yet now they manifested in a heightened and doubly lethal form. Everywhere potential turned to talent, talent to mastery, mastery to supernatural prowess. The stage was set for the sacred phoenix of the Aeldari race to rise once more.

THE ANCIENT AND THE NEW

Some amongst the imperilled Aeldari race believe they can be saved from the brink of oblivion by the awakening of Ynnead, the God of the Dead. By harnessing the strange spirit magic of this rising deity and drawing upon the energies of the slain, they wage their crusade with exceptional vigour and aggression.

It is said the Aeldari pantheon is long shattered, destroyed by their mortal followers' hubris and the galactic terror that is Slaanesh. Their pride was arguably justified, for the Aeldari once ruled over much of the galaxy, content that when they died they would be reincarnated. But their mastery over the material realm ultimately led to ennui, and a dangerous complacency. In their search for ever-more esoteric experiences, they plumbed depths of sensation and profligacy so dark their society began to spiral out of control. Unbeknownst to that ancient race, the roiling emotions of their depravities were coalescing in the warp. There they took form as a newborn god – Slaanesh, the Dark Prince of Excess, known to the Aeldari as She Who Thirsts.

The ascension of Slaanesh was a cataclysm of galaxy-splitting magnitude. In a single instant, the psychic shock wave of the Dark God's birth destroyed the most part of the Aeldari empire and triggered a permanent warp storm of unprecedented size. Even now that tempest roils between realspace and the warp at the northernmost end of the Great Rift, the region known to Mankind as the Eye of Terror. Within that nightmarish realm are the crone worlds, haunted planets that were once the jewels in the Aeldari empire's crown.

The true doom of the Aeldari came in a more insidious form. As the Asuryani tell it, their metaphysical cycle of reincarnation was severed by the violence of Slaanesh's birth, and gods that once ruled over them consumed. After a titanic duel with Slaanesh, Khaela Mensha Khaine – the Aeldari god of war – was shattered into a thousand pieces.

The others members of their pantheon, barring the Laughing God Cegorach, were devoured by the newly emergent Slaanesh. From that point on, when an Aeldari died, their soul would be likewise consumed by She Who Thirsts, a destiny far worse than oblivion.

The various factions of the Aeldari have sought ways to escape this fate, or at least allay it for a time. The Asuryani, for instance, wear psychocrystalline waystones that act as safe havens, absorbing their souls upon the moment of death.

Later these spirit stones are interred within a craftworld's infinity circuit, allowing the soul to transfer to a construct of relative safety and from then on spend existence in a safe but lifeless grey limbo.

The Drukhari instead ensure others suffer in their stead, a devil's bargain that only postpones their inevitable consumption by Slaanesh. Small wonder that many Aeldari hailing from either faction were quick to seize on the possibility that there was another way to evade their nemesis – and perhaps conquer it forever. This they called Ynnead.

There is an ancient and controversial school of thought regarding mortality in Asuryani

society, recently brought back to prominence by the prophecies of Kysaduras the Anchorite. It posits that when every one of the Aeldari race has died and passed into the infinity circuits of the craftworlds, their departed spirits will form a gestalt consciousness. In doing so they will awaken and empower a god, a deity of the dead with the power to defeat Slaanesh and end She Who Thirsts' baleful curse. Some amongst the Asuryani claim that though the time of ending is nigh, not all Aeldari must die to escape Slaanesh's clutches – that there is a hidden path to be found amongst the darkness. Foremost amongst these is Eldrad Ulthran, High Farseer of Craftworld Ulthwé.

Upon the crystal sands of the moon Coheria, Eldrad put into motion the grand plan that would alter the course of his race's destiny. Under the cover of their roving visitations, the Masque of the Midnight Sorrow – acting on the instructions of Eldrad – abducted the crystallised bodies of long-departed Farseers from each craftworld's Dome of Crystal Seers. These they took to Coheria, for Eldrad had identified the moon as a site of extreme psychic potential.

By harnessing Coheria's pure crystal sands and using each grain as a miniature spirit stone, Eldrad intended to perform a grand ritual wherein he would summon every departed spirit from every craftworld at the same time. The stolen Farseers' remains would provide potent hyperspatial links – though the transfer would rob all power and light from the donor craftworlds for a time, Eldrad judged the sacrifice worthwhile. With such a vast concentration of

departed souls in one place at one time, the High Farseer intended to awaken Ynnead prematurely and set him against the Aeldari's eternal nemesis.

Perhaps, if Eldrad's machinations had been completed, he would have succeeded in his immensely ambitious plan. But the elite xenos-hunters of the Deathwatch had followed the actions of the Ulthwéans for many years. Led by the prescient Brother-Captain Artemis, they launched a sudden strike against Eldrad and his allies just as he was conducting his grand ritual. Forced to protect himself from a searing plasma blast, the High Farseer lost focus. In the swirling tides of the warp, the composite sentience of slumbering Ynnead stirred, but did not awaken. From that partial apotheosis a fragment of the greater consciousness was born – an animus that soon possessed a warrior-dancer known as Yvraine. She became the high priestess of a new religion, and has since led her followers across the stars, uniting Asuryani and Drukhari behind her as she goes.

After becoming invested with Ynnead's power, Yvraine became able to draw the departing souls of those around her into herself, where they live on – not as half-real revenants or echoes of a former glory, but as willing allies. To outsiders, it seems as if Yvraine is talking to herself, listening to voices only she can hear, or changing personality in a heartbeat. Those who do not know of her creed think her insane, but the Ynnari know the truth: Yvraine's body harbours not just her own soul, but many others.

The Reborn who follow Yvraine's lead – the devoted warrior known as the Visarch and the dread avatar known as the Yncarne foremost amongst them – share her uncanny ability. They wear the spirit stones of the dead upon their person, drawing upon the energy and wisdom of the departed in times of need. With the doom of the Aeldari close at hand, their need for that deathly strength is greater than ever before.

> 'The tapestry of fate has been wrenched, torn, and unravelled, just as when Dariachna tore at her woven masterwork in a fit of madness. The question remains – in such times of upheaval and unpredictability, can new strands of hope be found?'
>
> – The Visarch

SKEIN OF STARS

HALO STARS

SCARUS SECTOR

1

CALIXIS SECTOR

FINIAL SECTOR

SEGMENTUM OBSCURUS

The Shackling

NAOGEDDON

DIMMAMAR

CYPRA MUNDI

MORDIAN

STORM OF THE EMPEROR'S WRATH

GOTHIC SECTOR

Ulthamar's Vengeance

VALHALLA

The Eye of Terror

BELIAL IV

CHINCHARE

CADIA

5

VIGILUS

PISCINA

4

Coheria

ALARIC

BAAL

Sangua Terra

AGRIPINAA

6

Cadmus Tertius

ELYSIA

MOLOV

NECRON MEPHRIT DYNASTY

CICATRIX MALEDICTUM

UPSILON

ARMAGEDDON

VORDRAST

2

SEGMENTUM SOLAR

ZANDROS

LASTRATI

GOLGOTHA

3

SEGMENTUM PACIFICUS

Terra & Mars

RYZA

CATACHAN

The Maelstrom

DOLOROSA

GATHALAMOR

URSULIA

MACHARIA

NECROMUNDA

DURIEL

ULTIMA MACHARIA

KRIEG

Gravian Prime

Luther McIntyre

Battle of two hundred Pyres

UHULIS SECTOR

OPHELIA

TALLARN

The Swordwind Purges

NOCTURNE

BALOR

V'RUN

Siren's Storm

Moon of Nightmares

ALEUSIS

Sea of Dead Stars

SOLSTICE

BANE'S LANDING

RYNN'S WORLD

NEPHILIM SECTOR

Even as darkness rushes in to claim the stars the scattered remnants of the ancient Aeldari empire battle for survival. Far-flung are their war zones, desperate their wars. Yet that desperation fans the flames of Ynnead's faith; more Aeldari adopt the Ynnari teachings every day, channelling the intense fervour of their people's psyche into this slim hope of victory.

SEGMENTUM TEMPESTUS

REDUCTUS SECTOR

AGRAX

Three Sisters

BAKKA

ANTAGONIS

Gryphonne IV

SAN LEOR

ILLUSTRIS

THE VEILED REGION

LYRIAX

NAIATOC

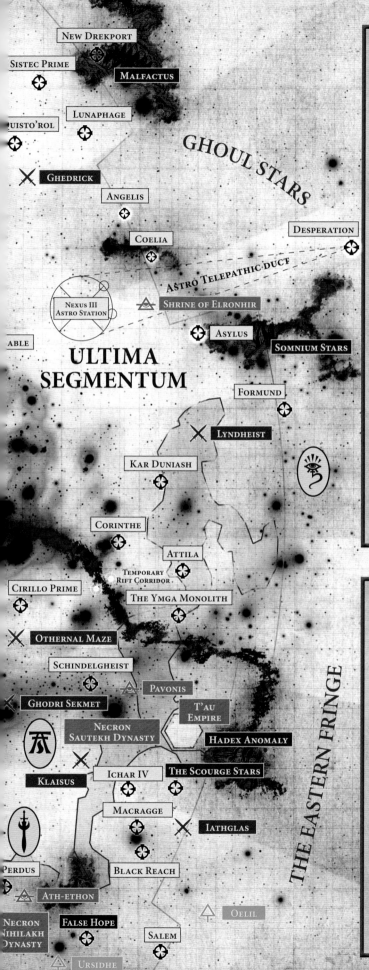

GHOUL STARS

NEW DREKPORT

SISTEC PRIME

MALFACTUS

QUISTO'ROL

LUNAPHAGE

GHEDRICK

ANGELIS

COELIA

DESPERATION

ASTRO TELEPATHIC DUCT

SHRINE OF ELRONHIR

NEXUS III ASTRO STATION

ASYLUS

...ABLE

ULTIMA SEGMENTUM

SOMNIUM STARS

FORMUND

LYNDHEIST

KAR DUNIASH

CORINTHE

ATTILA

TEMPORARY RIFT CORRIDOR

CIRILLO PRIME

THE YMGA MONOLITH

OTHERNAL MAZE

SCHINDELGHEIST

PAVONIS

GHODRI SEKMET

T'AU EMPIRE

HADEX ANOMALY

NECRON SAUTEKH DYNASTY

KLAISUS

ICHAR IV

THE SCOURGE STARS

MACRAGGE

IATHGLAS

PERDUS

BLACK REACH

ATH-ETHON

NECRON NIHILAKH DYNASTY

FALSE HOPE

SALEM

OELIL

URSIDHE

THE EASTERN FRINGE

1. Deep in the Halo Stars, Craftworld Yme-Loc matches its super-heavy Engines of Vaul against the Daemon Engine factories of Warpsmith Ur-Shellax.

2. Iybraesil's matriarchy sends a strike force of ten Howling Banshee shrines into the Eye of Terror, their mission to track down Jain Zar and remind her that her true duty lies with her Asuryani disciples, rather than the emergent Ynnari cult. None return unchanged by the experience.

3. Craftworld Il-Kaithe, its Bonesingers dispatched en masse to the war against Waaagh! Zagblasta, falls to a strange ailment. The light of a Chaos-tainted star slowly denatures the world-ship's wraithbone, causing strange coral-like growths to erupt along its length. With so few Bonesingers to tend it, the craftworld sickens. Its people are beset by a madness that sees them plunge into a series of near-suicidal engagements.

4. The Autarchs of Lugganath, appalled by the opportunistic Drukhari raids erupting in the wake of the Chaos-led Piscina Massacres, launch a retributive strike on behalf of their former Imperial allies. An escalating war rages between craftworlder and Commorrite even as the Chaos fleet returns to deliver the killing blow.

5. An assassination by the Wild Riders of Saim-Hann aimed at preventing a Chaos cult taking over the world of Vigilus sees them come under fire from Imperial forces unaware of their true motives. The Asuryani's revenge is bloody and swift. Only by sacrificing the ruling council to blame for the strike do the Imperial war leaders avoid outright war.

6. Craftworld Altansar fights alongside Imperial forces in defence of Sangua Terra, taking its fleet to battle against the *Planet Killer*'s armada even as it emerges from the Great Rift.

NOTABLE AELDARI ACTIVITY SITES

 Craftworld Ulthwé

 Craftworld Yme-loc

 Craftworld Alaitoc

 Craftworld Altansar

 Craftworld Biel-Tan

 Craftworld Lugganath

Craftworld Saim-Hann

Craftworld Kaelor

 Craftworld Il-Kaithe

 Craftworld Iyanden

 Craftworld Iybraesil

 Craftworld Mymeara

 Exodite world

 Monitored site

 Major conflict

THE HUNTER UNLEASHED

The ripples of causality, confusion and desperate hope that spread throughout Aeldari society caused waves of raw emotion to be reflected in the Realm of Chaos. Slaanesh, attuned like no other to the echoes of the Aeldari soul, peered through hooded eyes at the shifting destiny of that ancient race, and began to plan anew…

Though all the Aeldari loathed and feared Slaanesh, the god they knew as She Who Thirsts had a deep spiritual connection with the Aeldari, and it longed for their souls upon their death. So it was that the rise of the Ynnari did not escape Slaanesh's notice. The God of the Dead they worshipped, and the lack of vitality it represented, was anathema to Slaanesh. Here was a newly rising, morbid god that could steal the delicious soul-fodder of the Aeldari from Slaanesh once and for all.

This potential had already been proven beyond a doubt upon Biel-Tan, where the daemonic invasion and subsequent shattering of the Infinity Circuit had not yielded the feast of sweetmeats Slaanesh

had hoped for, but a dry, dusty feeling of absence. Instead of empowering the Dark Prince, all that bountiful soul energy had been given form as the Yncarne, Avatar of the Whispering God. Upon the crone world of Belial IV, that same morbid entity had banished a coven of Keepers of Secrets with an ancient Cronesword. Even the high priestess of this slumbering god had committed soul-theft, a crime that no true god could endure. Yvraine had become a walking mausoleum, harbouring hundreds of those spirits Slaanesh craved so deeply. The Dark Prince desired to devour her and the Yncarne more than any other prey.

There was opportunity for Slaanesh in the twisting tides of fate. Many

Asuryani – and even self-serving Drukhari – had converted to the cause of Ynnead. In embracing Ynnead, they were casting aside the shields of self-denial that had served them so well for so long.

It was true that should every one of the Aeldari give themselves to Ynnead, the Whispering God would awaken, and Slaanesh's power be broken. But should Yvraine and the Yncarne be hunted down and slain, Ynnead's tenuous existence would fade into allegory. The Aeldari that had stepped away from their precious paths would not reach the afterlife of Ynnead at all upon their deaths – but instead topple from their tightropes of self-discipline to plummet into the waiting maw of Slaanesh.

There was one creature in Slaanesh's employ that specialised in the killing of demigods and avatars. That being was Shalaxi Helbane, the Monarch of the Hunt. Banished from living memory some six hundred years ago by the Daemon hunters of the Grey Knights, Shalaxi had languished for centuries in the vast and sprawling Palace of Punishments. Now, with the atonement for that past failure at an end, it was time for the Greater Daemon to rise once more, enter realspace and slay the prophets of Ynnead. In doing so, Helbane would earn the favour of the Dark Prince once more.

After gathering many old allies – amongst them the vengeful symbiote Syll'Esske and a coterie of Slaaneshi Heralds – Helbane entered the webway, three dozen Fiends trilling in delirious joy behind the war party. The hunt was on. With Shalaxi's synaesthetic ability to blend a supernatural array of senses, Yvraine's soul-trail was soon picked out. Shalaxi's loping stride accelerated into a headlong sprint – one that did not slow over time, nor halt for rest, for when the will of their patron is behind them, Daemons do not tire. Dark dreams began to haunt Yvraine's nights.

It was upon the dead world of Threccia that Helbane launched its first vicious attempt upon the Aeldari prophet's life. Yvraine was travelling in the company of a warhost of Biel-Tan, braving a dash along a chain of webway gates that leapfrogged in quick succession across the executed planets of the Cursoai Reach.

Helbane's ambush struck with blistering speed, just as the Aeldari host was exiting one such wraithbone portal into a rocky valley of lifeless dust and wind-scoured statues.

Two spearheads of Slaaneshi Daemons swept down from the high passes above the valley, one encircling the rear of the Biel-Tan while the other swept around to their fore. Seeker Chariots rattled headlong into the Asuryani, their assault so swift that even the whip-quick craftworlders could not respond in time. Blood and spinning limbs flew as the sleek war engines drove deep into the Biel-Tan formation.

The narrow webway routes the Asuryani followed had prevented them from fielding grav-transports. They were thus forced to cut their way out of the ambush on foot. To these faithful Ynnari, Yvraine's life was paramount; as Helbane cut an unstoppable red path towards the prophet, the host's Farseer divided his forces. Screaming their dirgesong, a spearhead of Howling Banshees joined Yvraine in performing a dance of lashing blades that slit a neat hole in the daemonic ranks and allowed them to dash up the valley towards the next webway portal. At the same time, the main strength of the Biel-Tan host hurled themselves at the Slaaneshi Daemons. It was a suicidal attack, and Helbane ripped its way through the Aeldari at a ferocious rate. Yet their very deaths empowered Yvraine even as they proved the devotion of the Ynnari to their cause. Lent impossible speed by the dead souls flowing into her mortal vessel, Yvraine outstripped even the Slaaneshi Daemons, escaping into the webway and leaving Helbane raging in her wake. It had been a desperately near thing, but the prophet of Ynnead had escaped her hunter, at least for now. Helbane would not be denied forever, however.

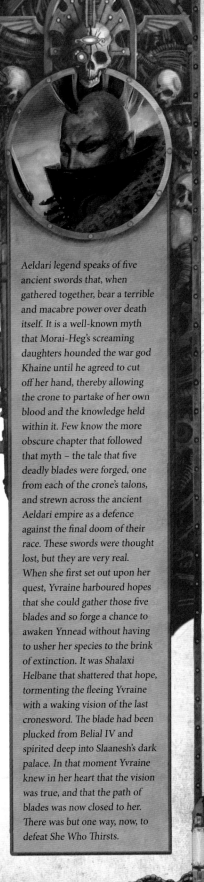

Aeldari legend speaks of five ancient swords that, when gathered together, bear a terrible and macabre power over death itself. It is a well-known myth that Morai-Heg's screaming daughters hounded the war god Khaine until he agreed to cut off her hand, thereby allowing the crone to partake of her own blood and the knowledge held within it. Few know the more obscure chapter that followed that myth – the tale that five deadly blades were forged, one from each of the crone's talons, and strewn across the ancient Aeldari empire as a defence against the final doom of their race. These swords were thought lost, but they are very real. When she first set out upon her quest, Yvraine harboured hopes that she could gather those five blades and so forge a chance to awaken Ynnead without having to usher her species to the brink of extinction. It was Shalaxi Helbane that shattered that hope, tormenting the fleeing Yvraine with a waking vision of the last cronesword. The blade had been plucked from Belial IV and spirited deep into Slaanesh's dark palace. In that moment Yvraine knew in her heart that the vision was true, and that the path of blades was now closed to her. There was but one way, now, to defeat She Who Thirsts.

THE FATES OF THE CRAFTWORLDS

The Asuryani world-ships were caught in the teeth of the tempest that was shaking the cosmos. Some amongst them were steering through the storm, and guiding their people to places of relative safety. Others faced dark fates, or were forced to adapt to near-constant war, by the strife heralded by the Dathedian.

After the Ynnari's desperate resurrection of Prince Yriel turned defeat into victory during the daemonic attack upon Craftworld Iyanden, they made haste to Macragge, there to bolster Humanity's shield against the scourge of Chaos. From there they defended a clutch of worlds from the scourge of Chaos, but always they were on the lookout for more Aeldari sympathetic to their cause.

On the proud craftworld of Saim-Hann, Yvraine found no small number of converts. The world-ship had been sorely pressed since the coming of the Great Rift. At the height of the Blood Crusade, it had sent five entire clans to hold back the gore-maddened Red Tide on Upsilon, securing a fraught victory before disappearing to leave the planet's human survivors shaken and confused behind them. At the same time the craftworld's fleet had fought void battles against Imperial navy ships and elements of Abaddon the Despoiler's armada.

At first Yvraine's call to arms was seen as the last thing the seers and chieftain of the craftworld needed. It risked a schism dividing their clans, for tempers on Saim-Hann had always run hot. A council was convened at the Speaking Place, a tribal hub in the midst of one of the craftworld's wilderness zones. Beneath the shimmering vault of a colossal bio-dome they talked of ancestors, spirits, and futures yet to be. For a while, they found accord around the ever-burning fires of that place. Then the skies shimmered above the conflagration, and a Drukhari strike force burst from a webway gate long forgotten. Their intent was to slay Yvraine with a swift decapitating strike.

The Drukhari's blades did not find their mark, for none other than the Phoenix Lord Jain Zar appeared to meet them in battle. The peace talks turned to fierce battle in moments, and the Ynnari were forced to flee.

Meantime, the craftworld of Alaitoc was preoccupied with its own missions and agendas. Even with the sky stained with the lifeblood of the cosmos and the scions of Chaos appearing in nigh every vision and prophecy, the puritan leaders of the world-ship espoused their long-held belief that it was the Necrontyr who posed the greatest threat to the galaxy at large. They had scried the unravelling threads of the future in their own way, and found a geometric void that threatened to swallow all. Alaitoc's foremost visionary, Ylocu Shaie, had written the Prophecy of Risen Doom whilst half-conscious in a fever dream, the intensity of the vision all but crippling her. Though it had taken her a lifetime to isolate the strand of potentiality that led to her worst nightmare, she had found it just the same, and it was of shocking potency. Shaie had brought her latest findings to the Seer Council of Alaitoc, singing of the Sea of Dead Stars at the climax of the hearing. Sobered by the vista she painted, they accelerated their plans to allay the threat of

the Necrons before their ancient enemies fully awoke – even though they drastically weakened their craftworld's defences as a result. In doing so they destroyed the Hyrekh Dynasty on the very day of its ascension, killing the Necrons with systematic, overlapping strikes whilst they still clawed their way from the slumber of stasis. With the pathfinder Illic Nightspear as their ambassador, they dealt extensively with the Harlequins of the Frozen Stars, whose agenda aligned with their own. In doing so, they found they had but scratched the surface of a far larger threat.

Even as they fought the Necrontyr on a dozen new fronts, the strike forces of Alaitoc were ambushed by the terror legions of the Slaaneshi Greater Daemon Sli'tha. The Daemon monarch intended to strike at Alaitoc whilst it was vulnerable, yet found that the information network provided by the craftworld's ranger cliques made it all but impossible to execute. Every time Sli'tha sent steed-riding Daemonettes on a mission of reconnaissance, they were picked off by pinpoint sniper fire that banished them back to the empyrean before they could report back to their masters. With the Pathfinders of Alaitoc leading their Rangers in dozens of wars across the Imperium Sanctus – that region of the Imperium that remained upon the Terran side of the Great Rift and was still illuminated by the light of the Astronomican – the main body of Craftworld Alaitoc was left free to take the fight to the Necrons of the Eastern Fringe.

Craftworld Biel-Tan had its fate intrinsically linked with the precarious rise of the Ynnari. Since

precarious rise of the Ynnari. Since the sundering of the wraithbone endoskeleton that formed its infinity circuit, the moon-sized Aeldari world-ship had slowly broken up into its constituent parts. Now Biel-Tan was more a fleet than a single ship, its strength almost halved by the turmoil that started upon the corrupted paradise world of Ursulia. They had reached the point of civil war by their fracture and the division that Yvraine had brought unto them – for a good portion of those lost to Biel-Tan had followed her lead to become Ynnari, further worsening the already reeling craftworld's situation.

Self-belief was their salvation, a quality that the remaining Asuryani held as one of the highest of all virtues. Its people, fierce optimists one and all, believed the Aeldari empire would rise like a phoenix from the ashes of near extinction. Biel-Tan was soon to show its strength, making a virtue of its ability to spread its power across a wider area than ever before.

During the Chaos invasion of the trio of Exodite worlds known as the Three Sisters, Biel-Tan was led to war by three of the legendary Phoenix Lords: Baharroth, Fuegan and Karandras. Both Baharroth and Fuegan were welcomed with fierce joy, for the coming of but one of Asuryan's pupils was cause for intense celebration, let alone two. But when Karandras revealed himself mid-battle upon Khazhar to cut a bloody swathe through a wedge of Daemon cavalry, a ripple of unease undercut the Asuryani's feeling of jubilation at his arrival. It was prophesied that at the time of the Rhana Dandra – that final, apocalyptic battle against Chaos that would spell the doom of everyone and everything – all six Phoenix Lords would fight together. Would three become six, showing that time of ending to be close at hand?

With the three Phoenix Lords working together at the fore, Biel-Tan levelled the Swordwind with such vengeful ferocity the Daemon hosts were broken and destroyed. In the weeks that followed, the human cultists upon nearby Khazhar – whose ritual-practising leaders had conjured the Daemons into realspace in the first place – were killed. The rest of the planet's population were slain by a psychic tempest unleashed by a conclave of Farseers and Warlocks that scoured their world clean of every last living thing. It was a display of raw power that lit the flame of war in the broken heart of Biel-Tan once more.

The leaders of Biel-Tan learned much from the Exodite kings of the Three Sisters. Conversely, many of the maiden worlds' youthful warriors were entranced by the sight of the Phoenix Lords. Through these legendary leaders, many young and vital Exodites were convinced that their aid was of paramount importance – the hour was so dire that the Aeldari race had to call upon every blade it could muster. Though their lieges raged at the betrayal, the young Exodites rode to war alongside the Swordwind. Just as the Biel-Tani had worked tirelessly to defend the maiden worlds of their former empire, now the Exodites would repay the debt in kind.

> 'We squandered our best chance to rise by hiding so long in the dark. No more, my kin. No more.'
>
> – Maegrah Worldsinger

ULTHWÉ'S MERCY

The Asuryani of Craftworld Ulthwé were known as the Damned, for they had fought against Chaos for far too long. Their methods were not always direct, as the Imperium found out to its cost.

+++ Ordovoxian
Transmission +++
Emperor's Day, 12 Post OCM

A strike force of Aeldari clad in black armour emerged from the Perditas Zone just as we engaged the forces of the Screaming Serpent. The xenos used our assault as a distraction, harrying the foe's flanks as we charged into the killing sonic blasts of the heretics holding the centre. The Aeldari's cursed xenotech proved effective against the footsoldiers of the Grand Cacophony. Even the hissing streams of discs released from their sidearms somehow cut through the ceramite armour of the traitor host where good honest lasfire had failed us. For a time, we allowed ourselves to believe the Nodum Psykana could be saved.

Then came the Screaming Serpent. Vast it was, its wings blocking out the sky. Its three swords cut men in half with each sweep. Its whip-hand simply beckoned, and I watched in horror as the Storm Troopers engaging it fell to their knees, then toppled face first into the mud. What that hated thing was, I can only guess, but it haunts my every waking moment. Something in my gut tells me I witnessed nothing less than ++ REDACTED+++

The scryers of Ulthwé were masters of foresight, and had read disaster in the stars long before the coming of the Great Rift. Even with all their artifice, these arch-manipulators were unable to allay the doom that was unfolding before them – only to mitigate its true and terrible potential.

Priding themselves on their subtlety, the Ulthwé Aeldari tipped the scales of conflict where they could, aiding the lesser races against the forces of Chaos in a hundred different war zones across the Segmentum Obscurus. It was their High Farseer Eldrad who was behind the amassing of the Crystal Seers and the events on Coheria that saw Ynnead shift in his slumber. For millennia the Seer Council of Ulthwé had masterminded the defence of the Eye of Terror and its surrounding planets, holding back the tide of Chaos until Abaddon's alliance of Chaos saw it finally torn apart. But perhaps their greatest coup was ensuring Yvraine reached the Shrine of Hera upon Macragge – first by a grand ritual that saw her borne across time and space, and then by force of arms when the Black Legion attempted to stop them. In this they allowed Yvraine to tear Roboute Guilliman from the brink of death. Upon Macragge, the Daughter of Shades used Ynnead's power to give the Primarch a new lease of life, combining Aeldari insight with Adeptus Mechanicus artifice to sustain the Primarch indefinitely. That act saw the Imperium of Man redefined. With the Primarch given aid enough to reach the Emperor's Palace upon Terra, and governance of Humanity's realm taken over by the one soul with mental strength and logistical skill enough to hold it together, Humanity was given the wherewithal to hold back the tide of Chaos – for a time, at least. Though they had done so by methods so indirect that none suspected their intervention, the seers of Ulthwé had created a shield against the scourge of Chaos so broad and so strong it had borne the weight of a hundred invasions and still not shattered. Yet even the finest bulwark will fall apart under the relentless tide, and even Ulthwé was not infallible.

The scryers of Ulthwé sifted the visions that entered their minds when they let their consciousnesses drift along the landscape of the future, picking out those fault lines where a concerted attack could shatter their plans. Some of those Imperial planets they watched over were corrupt, their masters looking after only their own interests as their cities and people burned around them. On these, the Ulthwéans resorted to that most desperate of all courses of action – direct intervention. Planetary governors and councillors who were too corrupt or slow-witted to stop their people from falling to Chaos were attacked by Black Guardian warhosts and stealthy Aspect Warrior forces who slew the leaders of each failing enterprise. In this, the craftworld ensured its targets' replacement, usually with more competent individuals inspired to proactivity by the shocking demise of their predecessors. The worlds that Ulthwé attacked found themselves ruled capably once more, each planet a stronger link in a chain that would hold back the tide of Chaos for a little longer.

THE ADONIS PALACE MASSACRE

The culling of Imperial incompetents was not a plan without cost in Aeldari lives. Merciless indeed were the methods of Ulthwé's Seer Council, for they prized speed and efficacy over slow and often fruitless diplomacy. This was especially true on the planet Cadmas Tertius, site of the Adonis Palace Massacre.

The first the Adonites knew of the Asuryani attack was the sudden appearance of a squadron of Hemlock Wraithfighters, escorted by Crimson Hunters from the Shrine of the Shrieking Squall. Descending from a shimmering, psychically formed cloud, the black Hemlocks threaded their way through a hail of anti-aircraft fire. In places they lost precious psyker-pilots to the sheer weight of fire, but the remainder bombarded the spiretips of the ruling cities with waves of crippling despair so intense they caused mass suicides within. The strike stopped a ritual of summonation performed by the narcissistic rulers of the planet – a grand spell of profane luxury intended to bring Slaaneshi Daemons into reality. In doing so, the assault prevented a split in realspace

that would have seen Cadmas Tertius infested by warpspawn, and later condemned to Exterminatus at the decree of the Emperor's Inquisition.

The planet's demise had been averted just in time, but those Aeldari emissaries who were sent to point this out to the new rulership were sent away at gunpoint. Instead of being welcomed as saviours, the black-clad Ulthwéans were called murderers and accused of grand regicide. Tempers flared, and harsh words exchanged. Though the Aeldari left, the matter was far from over.

The Adonites' replacements proved untainted by Chaos, though they were now hell-bent on taking revenge against the Aeldari. Under a false flag of parley, Adonis' naval resource approached the Asuryani who were still monitoring them in-system. Hugely outnumbered, several Ulthwé ships were blasted apart before the rest could slip into the darkness of the void, cursing the short-sighted nature of the humans they had given valuable lives to save.

WRATH OF COMMORRAGH

The hidden realm of Commorragh had been shaken to its foundations by the coming of the Dathedian and the warp quake that Yvraine had brought into its heart. Asdrubael Vect was out for revenge.

The Supreme Overlord of Commorragh had found himself in something of a quandary. The rise of Yvraine – and her transformation at the Crucibael arena into the high priestess of Ynnead – had triggered a metaphysical invasion that had allowed Daemon legions to spill into his artfully created city. Vect had isolated and effectively quarantined that invasion at great cost; even now that warp gate and its infernal spawn gnawed at the sub-realms conjured to hold it back. It was a great loss he would not ignore, and an insult he could not be seen to excuse. Vect could not strike directly at the Ynnari himself, however; to do so would be to acknowledge he considered them a threat. He worked instead through puppets and whispersmiths, layering intrigue and rumour atop one another until Kabals, Covens and Wych Cults alike moved against the Ynnari without ever realising that they did so at Vect's behest.

Some sought to directly assail those Ynnari dwelling within the fractured realm of Commorragh, and in so doing weaken or cast doubt upon Yvraine's cause. Such was the intent of Marquis Vulkhere of the Lords of Iron Thorn; by subtle whispers and shadowy missives it came to the Archon's attention that his hated rivals, the Kabal of Poisoned Hopes, had converted to the Ynnari cause and were gathering fresh recruits to their fortress in the Howling Spire. Vulkhere saw here a chance to eliminate his own long-time foes and give the appearance of making war upon the Ynnari without expending time and resources

hunting down Yvraine herself. Thus he unleashed his kill squadrons in a sudden and devastating assault upon the Howling Spire. Spearheads of grav-craft slid through the green-lit gloom around the spire, staying low amidst the lambent fog so that their sails cut through the fume like the fins of oceanic predators.

At the last moment some eldritch alarm warned the Ynnari of the approaching threat. The Howling Spire's defence guns spat darklight and hails of splinters, and in response grav impellers screamed and the Lords of Iron Thorn burst up from the mist-cover to attack. Lance blasts ripped back and forth as Ravagers jinked and wove, their gunners hammering the Howling Spire's defenders. Drukhari were atomised by energy beams that would have sundered tanks. Others toppled from the spire's flanks, their bodies riddled with toxic needles or bound in restricting webs of thorned metal. Return fire saw more than one gunship or transport explode in mid-air, shedding screaming bodies as its wreckage plummeted. However, striking fast and unheralded, the Iron Thorn swept the spire's lower galleries clear of defenders and landed a massive raiding party.

They were met by a ferocious counter-charge. The ragged alliance of Kabalites and Wyches who had flocked to the Ynnari banner fought back with the determination of true zealots. The Lords of Iron Thorn wavered as they found their opponents fighting with an unfettered death-madness even their pain-heightened reactions could not keep pace with. For long moments the battle hung in the balance, a blistering blur of violence engulfing every stairwell, walkway and torture chamber in the spire. Then came Marquis Vulkhere himself; whilst his foes were focused on the threat pushing up from below he and his hand-picked Trueborn bodyguard had blasted their way into the spire's upper chambers, slain Archon Leshh of the Poisoned Hope, and now fell upon the Ynnari from behind. Caught between two foes, hammered from without by the fire of the circling gunships, the Ynnari of the Howling Spire were annihilated.

This was but one example of the internecine warfare that erupted anew as disgusted or furious Drukhari turned upon the deviant death-cultists in their midst. Yet though the devotees of Ynnead found themselves beset, they were far from defenceless; conflict and violent rivalry is the norm in Commorragh, and this fresh schism

was but one more reason for the Drukhari to tear at one another. So it was that several sub-realms were claimed by pro-Ynnari factions, fortified against assault and became separatist enclaves in their own right. The message of Ynnead spread slowly through Commorragh, but despite Vect's best efforts, spread it did.

This was not Vect's only plan, of course. Through third-party brokers he offered impossibly rich rewards for Yvraine's severed head, and so spurred dozens of hunting parties and feral mercenaries to take up the prophet's trail.

Perhaps the deadliest such hunting party was led by Drazhar, Master of Blades. By following Yvraine to the sacred debating fires of Craftworld Saim-Hann and striking from a hidden webway portal, Drazhar got his blade a hand's breadth from the high priestess' neck. The kill strike was parried at the last moment by Jain Zar herself. The running battle that followed saw Asuryani, Ynnari and Drukhari clash in a series of engagements that took them to the ancient ruins of the Aeldari empire and beyond. Skilled as she was, Jain Zar could not overcome Drazhar in combat, for where she was a leader as well as a warrior, Drazhar was devoted to bladesmanship alone. But Jain Zar had pledged her power to the Ynnari, and with Ynnead's grace upon her, she fought with uncanny speed and skill to defend Yvraine. It appeared that even a mastermind such as Vect, allied with a near-mythical warrior such as Drazhar, could not engineer Yvraine's death. The Whispering God had use for his high priestess still, and he would not be denied.

THE GHODRI FALSEHOOD

Many of the Haemonculi that made their lair in the lower regions of Commorragh were old allies of Vect's. They were so steeped in the history of the Dark City, so influential in their control of the Drukhari's sham immortality, that they sought to maintain the status quo from which they had profited for so many centuries. The Prophets of Flesh, those who studied under the demented flesh-sculptor Urien Rakarth, had devised a new punishment – to take a transgressor and reshape them, melding their mortal clay until they looked, walked and even smelt like a human being. All Drukhari found this horrifying, for to them a human form was ungainly and ape-like, a cruel mockery of a biped in comparison to the lithe and alabaster-skinned Aeldari anatomy. This was a horrific punishment for a people so vain and haughty as the Drukhari, and those subjected to the treatment cried out that they would do anything at all to have it reversed. In these 'false humans,' Vect saw opportunity – one so twisted and sadistic that Urien Rakarth agreed to orchestrate it on his behalf.

On the slabcrete planet of Ghodri Sekmet, Yvraine preached the Ynnari creed to a hidden gathering of Alaitoc Pathfinders high in the peaks. The Aeldari did not expect any of the dull-witted humans who infested the planet to uncover the location of their eyrie, and Yvraine was speaking with such passion and fervour that all eyes were on her. Hence when the Imperial military announced their presence with a well-organised Astra Militarum pincer assault, the Aeldari found their line of retreat cut off by artillery fire. The Ynnari and Alaitoci fell back to the webway portal by which they had made planetfall upon Ghodri Sekmet – only to find a strike force of Drukhari mercenary elites bursting through. Caught between the hammer of the Drukhari assault and the anvil of the Astra Militarum – amongst whose ranks were Vect's false humans, who had engineered the attack – the Ynnari were decimated. Only the manifestation of the Yncarne, summoned to battle by so much death in one place, allowed the command structure of the Ynnari to break through and make their escape into the webway.

IYANDEN REBORN

The embattled craftworld of Iyanden had come close to having its flame snuffed out altogether. With the threat of Chaos writ large, its situation was made all the more precarious. In the Ynnari the craftworld saw a final chance to reverse their fortunes.

Time was running out for Craftworld Iyanden. In living memory it had weathered vicious attacks from Chaos armadas, endured headlong assaults from psychotic Ork Warlords and repelled the incursion of a major tendril of Hive Fleet Kraken. Then came N'Kisha. Even as the empyric darkness of the Noctis Aeterna clawed at the galaxy, this rapacious Keeper of Secrets employed its reality-bending energies to force passage into one of Iyanden's precious bio-domes. Asuryani reeled back in horror as a glowing rent a hundred feet high split the skin of reality amidst the dome's beautiful glades, and from within spilled the unfettered madness of the warp. Khornate Bloodcrushers and packs of Flesh Hounds loped out to hunt screaming Aeldari through the trees like game. Greater Daemons of Nurgle lumbered through the lovingly cultivated woodlands, chortling wetly as riotous rot spread out from them in all directions and waves of Plaguebearers trudged, droning their endless count, through the resultant mulch. Trilling Slaaneshi Daemons danced and span, meeting incoming squads of Guardians, Aspect Warriors and Wraithguard with deadly balletic grace and plucking out spirit stones like sweetmeats while Discs and Screamers of Tzeentch whipped overhead, their riders cackling madly and raining fire down on friend and foe alike.

First one bio-dome fell, then another, before the Daemons spilled out into the craftworld's labyrinthine interior to rampage at will. The Autarchs and Seers of Iyanden led the fight back with a desperate intensity, wielding phalanxes of Ghost Warriors like blades to cut through the swift-sprouting thickets of madness engulfing their craftworld. Yet they knew it was a losing fight, for their enemies were an ocean and the already depleted Aeldari ranks were not enough to stem the tide. It was the seeing-craft of their cousins that saved Iyanden in that

hour; just as all seemed lost a coalition of Harlequins and warhosts from a half-dozen other craftworlds plunged into the fight. They had braved the horrors of the Noctis Aeterna – suffering no small cost for doing so – and ridden to Iyanden's aid at the eleventh hour. Combined, the Aeldari forces were able to first contain the daemonic infestation and then to eradicate it one chamber, hall and corridor at a time. A conclave of Seers at last succeeded in closing the warp rift and, without their source of power, the Daemons flickered and faded. Yet there was little enough cause for celebration; Iyanden had been forced to rely upon others to ensure its survival yet again, and the allied Aeldari forces parted ways with no little bitterness and sense of mutual resentment.

When Yvraine brought news of the Ynnari creed to Iyanden, she was at first spurned. Yet when a Nurgle naval assault followed her arrival, it was Yvraine's summons of her old Corsair allies that saw the Chaos invasion blunted. Prince Yriel took the chance to lead a boarding action against the *Spawn of Oghanothir*, flagship of the Daemon Prince Gara'gugul'gor, and he struck with such deadly confidence that he penetrated right to the ship's heart. Plunging the Spear of Twilight into the ship's pulsing enginarium, he destroyed the half-sentient flagship from within. In return, he was dealt a mortal blow, Gara'gugul'gor smashing him with a heavy girder that killed him in a single strike. Yriel's body was recovered and brought back to Iyanden. Fortunately, the Angel of Iyanden, Iyanna Arienal, saw virtue in Yvraine's creed, and let her into Yriel's mausoleum. There the priestess burned out the plague with the energies of death and resurrected the prince with the power of rebirth. Once again Iyanden had been forced to rely on others for its salvation, but this time those saviours came with promise and proof that there could be another way.

'With Ynnead's grace, we gave the humans their demigod. A king reborn, with a deathly blade, just as the Anchorite's prophecy foresaw. Will it will buy us enough time to defeat our true foe? That is a truth that even Morai Heg herself could not forsee.'

- Prince Yriel of Iyanden, after the resurrection of Roboute Guilliman

Debate raged amongst the craftworld's Spiritseers in the wake of Yvraine's action. Many argued that if the Ynnari had the power of rebirth, and numbered Drukhari as well as Asuryani, then their combined mastery of body and soul could be enough to cross the river of death unmolested – denying Slaanesh in the process – only to emerge to a new life on the other side. A plan of vaulting ambition took form amongst the craftworld's council of elders, though others decried it as madness. The Arienal Hypothesis hinged on the fact that the Asuryani already had a safe haven in the form of their infinity circuit. Providing they mobilised sufficient Ghost Warriors to protect it, could not the entire craftworld cross the threshold of death? And if that was the case on one craftworld, could the rest of them follow suit at the same time? Iyanna Arienal argued that the Drukhari had ways to regrow physical forms wholesale from scraps of dead flesh, and that once the danger had passed the Aeldari souls could return to bodies of flesh and blood having cheated Slaanesh and empowered Ynnead. They could build their society anew, shorn of the spiritual curse that had haunted them these ten millennia.

It was a strong theory, but should it be proven fallible in practice it could see the craftworlds themselves shattered from the inside out. If the Ynnari were not there to absorb their spiritual essences, they would give Slaanesh a feast of souls like no other since the days of the Fall.

Long did the Dome of Crystal Seers resound to the sound of impassioned argument, with no one faction able to sway the other. Far beyond the bio-dome's crystal shell, a glowing, emerald circle grew ever larger. They neared the planet of Iathglas, site of a grand confluence of fate. There, Iyanden would fight as the champion of death itself.

'It is a simple truth. Only the dead can save the living.'

- Iyanna Arienal, the Angel of Iyanden

LAUGHING IN THE FACE OF DEATH

Many Harlequins saw a dark mirth in the dilemma presented to them by the Ynnari, for they saw themselves as already saved. Yet the opportunity to defeat Slaanesh forever was compelling indeed.

+++Auto-reliquary
Recovered+++
Transcript append+++

The warpspawn spilled out of that building like maggots from a corpse's gut. They were sickly white, and writhed over one another, screaming as if in some blind ecstasy. Amongst them was a god, or a goddess, I'm still not sure which, holding a spear as tall as a bastion, and just… horribly beautiful to look at. It gave a strange cry, like a hunting call. We could not concentrate. We just stood there, slack-jawed, with our lasguns held loose. Then there was a burst of scintillating light, and the spell broke. These flickering images of Aeldari, more like holographs than real warriors, appeared amongst the warpspawn. They fought hard, gave as good as they got. We came back to our senses, and battled alongside them as best we could. Some amongst those xenos things were dressed in skull masks and robes of deep red, more for a wake than for a battle. Wherever those ones trod, the corpses of dead xenos shivered and moaned around them. In the end we fled, I'm not ashamed to admit it. Haven't slept a wink since.

+++FRAGMENT ENDS
+++REGIMENT DEEMED
UNRECOVERABLE+++

The Harlequins had their own parts to play in the unfolding fate of the Aeldari. They had long opposed Slaanesh, and some amongst them had already thrown their lot in with the Ynnari. Some had linked the rise of the Ynnari to the prophecy from the crystal tome of Cegorach, unchained since the cataclysmic demise of the planet Dûriel. That eldritch book's last pages implied that Slaanesh's strength could not only be defeated, but turned against itself. Some Harlequins said that to place their hopes, their very souls, into the hands of a god yet to manifest was to walk across an abyss on a razored tightrope, or to dive breathless to the bottom of an ocean in the hope of finding a specific pearl. Yet even in the direst adversity, faith can thrive.

As with the craftworlds of the Asuryani, the great troupes of the Harlequins each had their own agendas and philosophies, and they did not always mesh well. Rather than get lost in debate, they simply acted upon their own initiatives. The Masque of Dreaming Shadow joined forces with Craftworld Alaitoc, voyaging to the galactic south in order to thwart the rising Necron threat, for they deemed it a more immediate peril than the implacable thirst of Slaanesh. The Masque of the Midnight Sorrow aligned themselves closely with Yvraine, as did the loose brotherhood of the Death Jesters. They worked amongst every troupe to keep the notion of Ynnead alive, for they believed that to bring a

god of the dead to prominence, and thereby destroy their ancient nemesis through the demise of that which had given it birth, would be the finest jest of all.

Cegorach's chosen had never worn the spirit stones of the Asuryani upon their chests. They believed that in return for utter devotion, the Laughing God would take them unto himself upon their deaths. In this, they had a similar theology to the Ynnari. They too had conviction enough to brave the perils of the galaxy on their own terms without safeguards and crystalline spirit stones to protect them. Indeed there were some amongst their number, known as Solitaires, who voluntarily walked the Path of Damnation, playing the part of Slaanesh in the ancestral plays of the Harlequins and devoting their lives to defeating that unholy power. It was these Solitaires that Yvraine sought amongst her Harlequin allies, for she had witnessed one such warrior duelling a Keeper of Secrets upon Belial IV, and his skill had left a deep impression upon her. Even then, she suspected that to secure the aid of a Solitaire would not be enough.

The daemonic hunter that had struck at Yvraine upon Threccia, and that she kept seeing in her recurring dreams, had proved unstoppable, both in reality and in every somnolent vision. In Yvraine's dreams first the Visarch, then the Yncarne, was cut to ribbons by the Daemon's assaults. Those Ynnari she had come to trust were slashed apart, impaled or pierced. Yvraine was last, the Daemon visiting a true death upon her that would see Yvraine's body crumble to ash and her soul swallowed whole by She Who Thirsts.

It seemed a fate inescapable. Yvraine still held out a slender hope nonetheless, for in the latest of her recurring nightmares, she was lucid enough to conjure the finest warriors of the Ynnari, Asuryani, Harlequins and Drukhari to mind – and in the phantom battles of her dreams they proved enough to defeat the mighty Daemon. The message was clear. Together, they would epitomise the most powerful aspects of the Aeldari psyche, and prove in microcosm that the Aeldari could defeat their hated enemy in this world and the next.

Yvraine began to gather her champions, those warriors who could be considered pre-eminent amongst the subcultures of the Aeldari race. The Visarch was already at her side; as ever, he would defend her with his life. The Yncarne would answer her summons should enough deathly energies saturate the battlefield. As for the Asuryani, she already had one stalwart protector, one who had already proved willing and able to defend her, in the form of Jain Zar. Lelith Hesperax had also sided with the Ynnari in exchange for a promise of eternal puissance – and with the vector of her immortality at risk of permanent death, the Succubus could be convinced to fight alongside the Daughter of Shades out of enlightened self-interest, also. But there was still one problem that stood between Yvraine and her intended scheme. Solitaires, spending the most part of their lives in costume as civilians of the Aeldari race, were masters in the arts of disguise. Securing the aid of one of Cegorach's chosen would be next to impossible.

In dreams, there came an answer. A pair of souls that Yvraine had perceived in her visions, searing through the threads of fate like a pair of binary stars, burned bright indeed. One was an Aeldari soul, the other a human psyker of incredible power – and both were getting closer with every passing day.

When Yvraine had been at her meditations upon the relic world of Iachi, the Visarch came to her, bowing his head and resting his forehead upon the pommel of the Sword of Silent Screams. He spoke of two exceptional individuals who sought audience with her. One was a handsome Aeldari with two longblades upon his back, and the other a human female in black power armour and whose hair was a shock of white. The latter was possessed of a psychic aura so powerful it stung the mind.

The Aeldari visitor, an exile from the favour of Cegorach, told Yvraine of a fresh cataclysm to come. The human female spoke of a hidden foe, and a force that would turn stars and souls black. Yvraine appeared to listen well, for the language of prophecy had become well known to her, but in reality she was focused only on the fate of the Ynnari. She agreed to lend the aid that the mysterious Aeldari requested of her – though she did not say when. In return, she bade the exile seek out those Harlequins of his former kin, ensuring that a Solitaire was found before it was too late. The deal agreed, the strange pair conjured a shimmering portal and stepped into the twilight between worlds once more.

HOPE AND DESPAIR ENTWINE

Through means both psychic and mundane, Yvraine had carefully sown the seeds of her plan through the subcultures of the Aeldari race. Every iota of her influence had been bent towards mustering for war at an old haunt of hers – there, on Iathglas, she would meet again the inescapable predator that sought to take her head.

The journey to Iathglas was fraught with warp storms. Those who approached through the webway found the strange translucent tunnels echoing to distant howls, whilst in space, veteran helmsmen were tested to their limits. In this the Aeldari saw a sign that they were on the right path – some even claimed that the storms were Slaanesh's influence, trying to hold them back. Sure enough, in places the ships were lost, becalmed, or set upon by Heretic Astartes, but the dauntless survivors forged through every obstacle laid in their path.

Vast, lambent and surrounded by a triad of dark moons, Iathglas was a paradise world in orbit around the reddish star of Miaghu. Yvraine remembered the planet well from her time as a Corsair queen. She had used it as a safe haven when hiding from her many enemies in the Segmentum Pacificus. Iathglas was beautiful to the naked eye, but when observed with the witch-sight, its spiritual importance became clear. A central world-shrine formed the heart of the planet's psychic nervous system. Yvraine made haste to the largest of their number, knowing that there she would find the Exodites she sought – for they had always been fiercely protective of their world-shrine.

There, the souls of all the departed Exodites from that maiden world rested in a psychic gestalt, a loose geomantic equivalent of an infinity circuit. It was this reservoir of spiritual energy that Yvraine intended to use as a shield against the inevitable, that hour when Slaanesh's hunt arrived. Amidst great formality she greeted the Exodite chieftains she had befriended in her former life as the

corsair Amharoc. Eventually the chiefs said they would not support Yvraine's plan, but neither would they stand in the way of it.

Over the last few months, those messengers Yvraine had sent abroad into the cosmos had reached their intended targets and, braving the dangers of the darkening galaxy, those she summoned had answered her call. More Aeldari had gathered upon Iathglas of their own volition, their Farseers reading the skeins of unwinding fate and either sending delegations in their stead or else coming to the world themselves at the head of power war hosts.

Some of the delegations made landfall around the planet's world shrine, and there soon fell to debating the course of the Aeldari race. Autarchs, Haemonculi, Shadowseers and many other Aeldari leaders delivered impassioned speeches or argued vociferously, though they came no closer to reaching an accord. Other parties hung back, groups such as the Kabal of the Obsidian Rose or the Masque of the Frozen Stars keeping their own counsel as they wandered Iathglas' wilds or lurked in orbit over the planet. All had come to answer the call of fate, and to effect the confluence of causality they knew was developing on Iathglas, but few sought the exact same outcome to this strange conclave.

Yvraine had expected such division, just as she had expected those who had chosen the path of Ynnead to come to her when she called. Jain Zar, Lelith Hesperax, a Troupe of the Midnight Sorrow including their cursed but deadly Solitaire, a fleet of Corsairs who hung in orbit, silent

and ready – all answered Yvraine's summons and attended her in person as she staged her own muster near to the world-shrine itself. Doom approached, Yvraine knew, but if she could defeat her fate with the aid of such an alliance of Aeldari factions she would perhaps provide her arguing race with an example that spoke louder than any words. Tense, ready, she waited for fate to run its course.

On the sixth hour of the sixth day of the sixth week since Yvraine's arrival, word came of daemonic incursion. An Exodite rider, mounted on a swift saurian beast and sorely wounded, rode hard into the clearing where Yvraine's army had gathered. He talked in panicked tones of a great massacre near the Equatorial Faneway. A towering Daemon led the invasion force, and it could not be stopped by Exodite, Asuryani or Drukhari alike. Even as the Exodite messenger succumbed to his wounds, the sky shimmered dark. The wind, howling through the trees, rose to a bone-chilling shriek. Suddenly a rain of sickly-sweet fluid pelted down, robbing visibility as the squall lashed the forest inside and out. Then, amongst the trees, a flicker of purple light flared – and the Daemon known as Shalaxi Helbane strode from the verdant wilderness.

Helbane advanced alone, prowling like a great hunting felid towards its prey. Yet the very visions that Yvraine had been tormented by for so long finally proved worth enduring. She had seen

this moment many times, knew what came next by heart and had already put orders in place for a coordinated response. Asuryani warriors and skimming tanks darted toward the southern edge of the clearing, Drukhari Wyches and Harlequins toward the north. They slammed headlong into surprised packs of Slaaneshi Daemons that had been about to spring forth in ambush. Ruby lances of laser fire stabbed down from the Corsair fleet in orbit to tear blazing holes in the forest canopy and annihilate more of the unnatural invaders. The Daemons' numbers were great, however, and they delighted in agony and risk as much as they thrilled at bloodshed and victory; undeterred, Helbane's vastly swollen hunting party fought back. Vicious gunfights, running skirmishes and lightning-fast duels erupted all along the tree line around the clearing.

Meanwhile, five champions ran to meet the Daemon, five souls burning bright against a living furnace of dark energy. Lelith Hesperax sprinted towards Helbane with jaw-dropping speed, knives bared, teeth glinting in a cruel smile. Yvraine and the Visarch followed close behind, Croneswords drawn. Behind Helbane the Solitaire somersaulted from the canopy in a blur of glimmering diamonds, whilst Jain Zar charged front and centre, her war shout rising.

The fight that ensued was the stuff of legend. Helbane was isolated from the wider Daemon horde by the determined battle-lines of Aeldari, who braved annihilation to launch one tactical riposte after another amidst the rain of Corsair fire. No other race could have dared such a precise and potentially disastrous style of

warfare, fighting in concert and perfect synchronicity, the Asuryani, Drukhari and Harlequins wove a dance of death between the searing energy columns that fell from the heavens and gutted every daemonic assault before it could break through the Aeldari lines. The fate of the conflict would be decided by the duel between Helbane and Yvraine's champions.

MISSIONS

'The Rhana Dandra. The end of
our race. How long have we said
it is inevitable? Every prophecy
points to its culmination. Yet
can it not be postponed? And is
our fatalistic acceptance of our
destruction the very thing that
will bring it about?'

- Theuria of Ulthwé

WARS OF THE AELDARI

The rules presented in this section allow you to play games set in locations inspired by those found in the narrative of this book, as well as play through some of the most dramatic and climactic battles involving the Aeldari in the period of the Psychic Awakening.

THEATRES OF WAR

Opposite you will find rules for two new theatres of war. These allow you to play games of Warhammer 40,000 in evocative environments that present exciting and unique new challenges to overcome.

Battles set at high altitude, such as atop the towering spires of a hive, will see warriors fighting on high platforms, with the surface beneath them becoming ever-more unstable as more and more destruction is visited upon it.

In conflicts on Aeldari maiden worlds, warriors of all races find themselves invigorated by the verdant energies of the planet's world-spirit. Those Aeldari who do battle there are often driven to new heights of rage by the destruction wrought upon the paradisical landscapes they seek to protect.

ECHOES OF WAR MISSIONS

On pages 28-33 you will find three new Echoes of War missions for your narrative battles. These allow you to refight key battles involving the Aeldari described in this book, from the ill-fated Ulthwé strike on the spire of Adonis to Yvraine confronting her daemonic pursuer, Shalaxi Helbane. These missions can be combined with the theatres of war opposite to add an additional layer of depth to your games.

Players are also encouraged to use the rules that are presented here as a basis for their own Narrative Play missions, whether they are a part of the Aeldari's ongoing war for survival in the wake of the Great Rift, or simply represent other, similar battlefields upon which they wish their armies to do battle.

'The universe is tripartite: the sunlight of the material plane, the darkness of the spirit plane, and the twilight of the spaces betwixt the two.'

- Spiritseer Iyanna Arienal

THEATRES OF WAR

With the Great Rift splitting the firmament and their race's future looking ever-more bleak, the various sub-factions of the Aeldari found themselves forced to fight in a multitude of locations across the galaxy.

In this section you will find exciting new theatres of war to use in your games of Warhammer 40,000. Theatres of war offer new tactical challenges to enrich your games, and introduce new rules to represent many varied battle environments. Some modify the core rules – for example, by altering the range of weapons. Others provide new rules for phenomena like dust storms, volcanic eruptions and earthquakes. Others still grant additional abilities and Stratagems to certain units.

These rules are designed to reflect the theatres of war the Aeldari found themselves fighting in during the events described in this book. These rules are entirely optional and, so long as you and your opponent agree, they can be used in any Warhammer 40,000 game.

Agree which, if any, theatre of war rules will be used when you are setting up the battlefield, before deployment.

THEATRE OF WAR: MAIDEN WORLD

The maiden worlds are carefully crafted paradises that represent hope for the dwindling Aeldari. Those of that ancient race will fight to protect the precious few of these that remain unspoiled with a vicious fury.

Vigour of the World Spirit: At the end of your Movement phase, you can roll one D6 for each non-**Vehicle** unit from your army that is on the battlefield. On a 6+ you can select one model in that unit to regain 1 lost wound. If there is not a model in that unit that has lost any wounds, but any models from that unit have been destroyed, roll one D6; on a 4+ you can return one of those models to the battlefield with 1 wound remaining, placing it in unit coherency (if the model cannot be placed in this way, it is not returned to the battlefield).

Unspoiled Paradise: When a **Vehicle** model explodes, if there are any **Aeldari Character** models on the battlefield, randomly determine one of them and roll one D6, adding 1 if that **Vehicle** model has the **Aeldari** keyword. If that **Vehicle** model is an **Aeldari Building**, add 2 to the roll instead. On a 5+ that **Character** model is driven into a rage by the destruction visited upon the maiden world; add 1 to its Strength and Attacks characteristics until the end of the battle.

THEATRE OF WAR: HIGH ALTITUDE

Many worlds contain immense cities whose great spires are studded with platforms, or floating structures that harvest valuable atmospheric gasses. Battles conducted in such places are often brutal and perilous affairs.

Open Sky: Running along the edge of the battlefield is a 6" area that represents open sky. Only models with the **Fly** keyword can be set up in or move into this area. If a model without the **Fly** keyword is set up in or moves into this area for any reason, it is immediately destroyed. The area of the battlefield that is not open sky is referred to as the platform.

Destabilised Platform: When a **Vehicle** model on the platform explodes, after resolving the effects, roll one dice for each unit that does not have the **Fly** keyword and is within 9" of the edge of the battlefield. Add 2 to the result if the exploding model was **Titanic**. On a 5+ that unit suffers D6 mortal wounds as warriors tumble to their deaths or crash into railings.

Gusting Winds: At the start of the battle round, the player who has the first turn rolls one D6. On a 1-4, high winds are blowing towards the battlefield edge corresponding to the result as shown on the map below. In your Movement phase, you can add 6" to the Move characteristic of any models from your army with the **Fly** keyword. A model that has its Move characteristic increased in such a way must finish any move it makes that phase closer to the table edge the high winds are blowing towards than when they started the move.

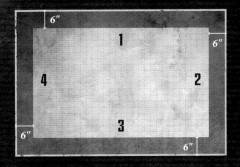

ECHOES OF WAR
SKYSTRIKE

To the defenders of Adonis, it had seemed as though it was a day like any other manning the defence guns of their hive spire. The next moment the skies were filled with screaming jets as xenos aircraft launched strikes against the spires of the planet's ruling elite. Even as the Imperial forces aligned their anti-air defences, more xenos warriors disembarked onto the platform to silence them…

THE ARMIES

Each player must first muster an army from their collection. The Defender commands the Astra Militarum defence force. The Attacker commands the invading Aeldari force. A player can include any models in their army, but if their army is Battle-forged they will also be able to use the appropriate Stratagems included with this mission (see opposite).

THEATRES OF WAR

Use the rules from Theatre of War: High Altitude (pg 27) to reflect the lofty platform upon which this battle is taking place.

THE BATTLEFIELD

The Defender creates the battlefield. The battlefield should resemble a spire-top platform, with a mixture of ruins and buildings. Set up four objective markers as shown on the deployment map to represent heavy anti-air guns. These should be in the open or on top of buildings.

DEPLOYMENT

After terrain has been set up, the Defender sets up their units wholly within their deployment zone. The Attacker then sets up their units wholly within their deployment zone. The Attacker can set up units in Reserve (see page 194 of the *Warhammer 40,000* rulebook). The combined Power Rating of the units set up in Reserve cannot exceed half of the player's army's Power Level.

FIRST TURN

The Attacker has the first turn.

SUSTAINED ASSAULT

The Attacker can use the Sustained Assault rules (see page 195 of the *Warhammer 40,000* rulebook). Units brought back to the battlefield using these rules must be set up wholly within 9" of the edge of the battlefield.

THE ANTI-AIR GUNS

The Attacker's units treat objective markers as enemy models. The objective markers have a Toughness characteristic of 7, a Wounds characteristic of 5, a Save characteristic of 4+ and a Leadership characteristic of 10. They are also considered to be **Character** units for the purposes of choosing a target for an attack (but for no other purposes). If an objective marker is destroyed, remove it from the battlefield.

At the end of the battle round, the Defender rolls three D6 for each objective marker remaining on the battlefield. For each 4+ they roll, they gain a Destroyed Aircraft point. Keep a tally of these points throughout the battle.

BATTLE LENGTH

Use the Random Battle Length rules (see page 194 of the *Warhammer 40,000* rulebook). If the Defender reaches a total of 15 Destroyed Aircraft points, or all four objective markers are destroyed, the battle ends immediately.

VICTORY CONDITIONS

If the battle ends immediately because the Defender has reached 15 Destroyed Aircraft points, the Defender wins a major victory. If the battle ends immediately because the Attacker has destroyed all four objective markers, the Attacker wins a major victory. Otherwise, if one army has been entirely destroyed, the other army's player wins a major victory. If neither player has won a major victory, then if there are two or more objective markers remaining on the battlefield, the Defender wins a minor victory. Any other result is a minor victory for the Attacker.

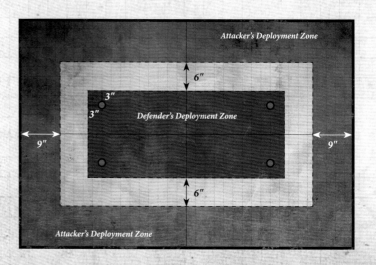

STRATAGEMS

In this mission, players can use Command Points (CPs) to use the following bonus Stratagems:

2CP — EVASIVE MANOEUVRES
Attacker Stratagem

Focussing their attack runs, the Aeldari pilots avoid the worst of the anti-air fire.

Use this Stratagem at the end of the battle round, before the Defender rolls to see how many Destroyed Aircraft points they gain. Subtract 1 from the result of each D6.

3CP — INTENSIFY FIRE
Defender Stratagem

Even in the fiercest battles, some officers manage to keep their head and direct their defences with skill.

Use this Stratagem at the end of the battle round, before rolling to see how many Destroyed Aircraft points you gain. You can re-roll all or any of the dice.

2CP — CAST THEM DOWN!
Attacker Stratagem

Fighting near the edge of the platform is fraught with danger…

Use this Stratagem at the end of the Fight phase. Select one enemy unit that cannot **FLY** that is within 1" of any units from your army and within 1" of the edge of the platform (see page 27). That unit suffers D3 mortal wounds.

2CP — CAST THEM DOWN!
Defender Stratagem

Fighting near the edge of the platform is fraught with danger…

Use this Stratagem at the end of the Fight phase. Select one enemy unit that cannot **FLY** that is within 1" of any units from your army and within 1" of the edge of the platform (see page 27). That unit suffers D3 mortal wounds.

1CP — DEMOLITIONS
Attacker Stratagem

Severing essential power couplings and securing grenades against exposed plating ensures rapid destruction of the defence turrets.

Use this Stratagem in your Shooting phase. Select one objective marker that is within 1" of any units from your army and roll one D6. On a 3+ that objective marker suffers D3 mortal wounds.

1CP — PROTECT THE GUNS
Defender Stratagem

Some of the defence force exemplify the ideals of the Imperium, sacrificing themselves to protect valuable assets.

Use this Stratagem in your opponent's Shooting phase, when an objective marker is selected as the target of an attack made with a ranged weapon. Until the end of that phase, when that objective marker would lose any wounds as a result of an attack made against that marker, you can select one unit from your army that is within 3" of it and roll one D6; on a 4+ that objective marker does not lose any wounds and the selected unit suffers 1 mortal wound for each of those wounds.

ECHOES OF WAR
BITTER REVERSAL

At Vect's command, a number of Drukhari were surgically altered to appear as Humans, and in this guise infiltrated several Astra Militarum regiments. Once in place, the agents of the Dark City managed to divert the guardsmen forces and manipulate them into tracking down and attacking Yvraine's Reborn followers. Unless the Ynnari can escape with all haste, they will likely be overwhelmed by the misled Imperial forces.

THE ARMIES

Each player must first muster an army from their collection. The Defender commands the Ynnari force, which must include Yvraine. The Attacker commands the Astra Militarum force manipulated by the Drukhari. A player can include any models in their army, but if their army is Battle-forged they will also be able to use the appropriate Stratagems included with this mission (see opposite). If the Attacker wishes to make use of the 'The Architects Revealed' Stratagem, they will require one or more Drukhari units with a Power Rating of 5 or less.

THE BATTLEFIELD

The Defender creates the battlefield. The battlefield should resemble the high peaks of the slabcrete world Ghodri Sekmet, where the battle takes place.

DEPLOYMENT

After terrain has been set up, the Defender sets up their units wholly within their deployment zone. The Attacker then sets up their units wholly within their deployment zones, divided as evenly as possible between deployment zone A and deployment zone B. The Attacker can set up units in Reserve (see page 194 of the *Warhammer 40,000* rulebook). The combined Power Rating of the units set up in Reserve cannot exceed half of the player's army's Power Level.

FIRST TURN

The Defender has the first turn.

THE WEBWAY GATE

Units from the Defender's army can leave the battlefield through the Webway Portal. If such a unit is within the area marked as the Webway Portal on the deployment map at the end of the Defender's Movement phase, the Defender can remove it from the battlefield. That unit is then said to have escaped.

BATTLE LENGTH

Use the Random Battle Length rules (see page 194 of the *Warhammer 40,000* rulebook) to determine how long the battle lasts. If Yvraine escapes or is destroyed, the battle ends immediately.

VICTORY CONDITIONS

If the battle ends immediately because Yvraine has escaped, the Defender wins a major victory. If the battle ends immediately because Yvraine has been slain, the Attacker wins a major victory. Otherwise, if one army has been entirely destroyed, the other army's player wins a major victory.

If neither player has won a major victory, then if, at the end of the battle, Yvraine has 2 or fewer wounds remaining, the Attacker wins a minor victory. Any other result is a minor victory for the Defender.

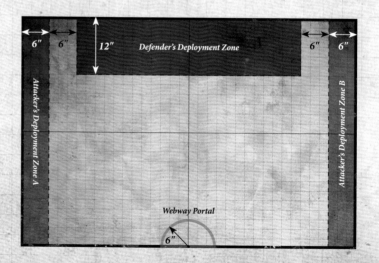

STRATAGEMS

In this mission, players can use Command Points (CPs) to use the following bonus Stratagems:

THE ARCHITECTS REVEALED

3CP

Attacker Stratagem

Stepping forth before the fleeing Reborn, the Drukhari strike them down before they could react.

Use this Stratagem at the end of your Movement phase. Set up one **DRUKHARI** unit with a Power Rating of 5 or less wholly within the area marked as the Webway Gate on the deployment map. If the unit cannot be set up wholly within this area, it is not set up.

CUT THEM OFF

1CP

Attacker Stratagem

Recon elements of your forces speed ahead to cut off the enemy retreat.

Use this Stratagem in your Movement phase, when a unit with the Fast Attack Battlefield Role Advances. Add 6" to the Move characteristic of that unit's models until the end of the Movement phase instead of making an Advance roll.

HEAD START

3CP

Attacker Stratagem

Receiving intelligence from unknown sources, your forces spring their trap with impeccable timing.

Use this Stratagem at the start of the battle, before the first battle round. You can take the first turn instead of the Defender.

FIGHT OR FLIGHT

2CP

Defender Stratagem

Desperate to escape, the Ynnari seek to extricate themselves from melee as swiftly as possible.

Use this Stratagem at the end of the Fight phase. Select one **YNNARI** unit from your army. That unit immediately Falls Back.

SHROUDED FROM VIEW

2CP

Defender Stratagem

Utilising the camouflage technologies of the Alaitoc forces, the Reborn hide themselves from their attackers.

Use this Stratagem at the start of your opponent's Shooting phase. Select one **YNNARI** unit from your army. Until the end of that phase, that unit can only be chosen as the target of a shooting attack if it is the closest enemy unit to the firing unit.

DIVINE ASSISTANCE

1CP

Defender Stratagem

Ynnead has been known to intervene to protect his chosen vessel in times of need.

Use this Stratagem at the start of your Psychic phase. Add 1 to Psychic tests taken for Yvraine until the end of that phase.

ECHOES OF WAR
CONFRONTATION

Confronted at last by Shalaxi Helbane and a coterie of fiends, Yvraine knew that flight was not an option. The only way to end this pursuit was to turn and fight. Rallying the greatest heroes of the Aeldari, Yvraine prepares to face her nemesis and prove to all that Slaanesh can only be defeated through unity.

THE ARMIES

Each player must first muster an army from their collection. The Defender commands the Aeldari force, which must include Yvraine and can only include **Character** models. The Attacker commands the Slaaneshi Daemon force, which must include Shalaxi Helbane, which has finally managed to corner its prey. A player can include any models in their army, but if their army is Battle-forged they will also be able to use the appropriate Stratagems included with this mission (see opposite).

THEATRES OF WAR

Use the rules from Theatre of War: Maiden World (pg 27) to reflect the planet upon which this battle is taking place.

THE BATTLEFIELD

The Defender creates the battlefield. The battlefield should be relatively open, with a scattering of trees to represent the wooded area of the maiden world in which the battle takes place.

DEPLOYMENT

After terrain has been set up, the Defender sets up their units wholly within their deployment zone. The Attacker then sets up their units wholly within their deployment zone. The Attacker can set up units in Reserve (see page 194 of the *Warhammer 40,000* rulebook). The combined Power Rating of the units set up in Reserve cannot exceed half of the player's army's Power Level.

FIRST TURN

The Defender has the first turn.

SUSTAINED ASSAULT

The Attacker can use the Sustained Assault rules (see page 195 of the *Warhammer 40,000* rulebook) for any units of **Fiends of Slaanesh**, **Seekers** or **Daemonettes**. Units brought back to the battlefield using these rules must be set up wholly within 6" of the Attacker's battlefield edge.

BATTLE LENGTH

Use the Random Battle Length rules (see page 194 of the *Warhammer 40,000* rulebook). If Yvraine is destroyed, the battle ends immediately.

VICTORY CONDITIONS

At the end of the battle, if one army is totally destroyed, the other army's player wins a major victory. Otherwise, if Yvraine has been destroyed, the Attacker wins a major victory. If Yvraine is still on the battlefield at the end of the battle, the Defender wins a minor victory.

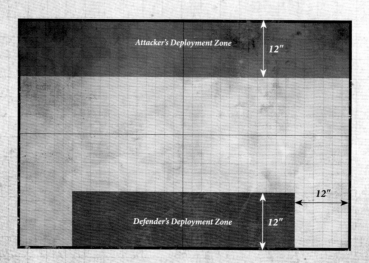

STRATAGEMS

In this mission, players can use Command Points (CPs) to use the following bonus Stratagems:

DESECRATION
1CP

Attacker Stratagem

The forces of Slaanesh take any opportunity to provoke the Aeldari into extremes of emotion.

Use this Stratagem at the end of your Movement phase. Select one woods terrain feature that is within 1" of a **SLAANESH** unit from your army. Subtract 1 from the Leadership characteristic of **AELDARI** models until the end of the battle. You cannot use this Stratagem on the same woods terrain feature more than once per battle.

PRECISION BARRAGE
3CP

Defender Stratagem

Following the battle from orbit, the corsair fleet employs its guns to aid its allies.

Use this Stratagem in your Shooting phase. Select one point on the battlefield. Roll one D6 for each unit within D6" of that point, subtracting 1 from the result if that unit is a **CHARACTER**; on a 4+ that unit suffers D3 mortal wounds. You can only use this Stratagem once per battle.

DESTROY THE REBORN
2CP

Attacker Stratagem

The Reborn's use of soul energy is taken as a grave insult by the forces of Slaanesh.

Use this Stratagem in any phase, when an **YNNARI** unit from your opponent's army begins drawing strength from death. Select one **SLAANESH** unit within 9" of that unit. Until the end of your next turn, when resolving an attack made by a model in that **SLAANESH** unit, add 1 to the hit roll.

POWER OF THE WORLD SPIRIT
2CP

Defender Stratagem

Channelling the power of the maiden world, the psyker focuses their powers.

Use this Stratagem in your Psychic phase, before an **AELDARI PSYKER** model from your army attempts to manifest a psychic power. Add 2 to the result of the Psychic test if that model is within 3" of any woods terrain features.

EXQUISITE AGONIES
1CP

Attacker Stratagem

The Daemons of the Dark Prince draw vigour from the pain of their prey.

Use this Stratagem at the start of the Fight phase. Select one **SLAANESH** unit from your army. Until the end of that phase, when an enemy model loses a wound as a result of an attack made by a model in the selected unit, roll one D6; on a 4+ that model in the selected unit regains 1 lost wound.

DESPERATE DEFENCE
3CP

Defender Stratagem

For the Aeldari, there is no worse fate than to be slain by a Daemon of Slaanesh.

Use this Stratagem in any phase, when a **CHARACTER** model from your army is destroyed. At the end of that phase, roll one D6; on a 4+ set up that model as close as possible to their previous position, with 1 wound remaining. This Stratagem cannot be used on the same model more than once per battle.

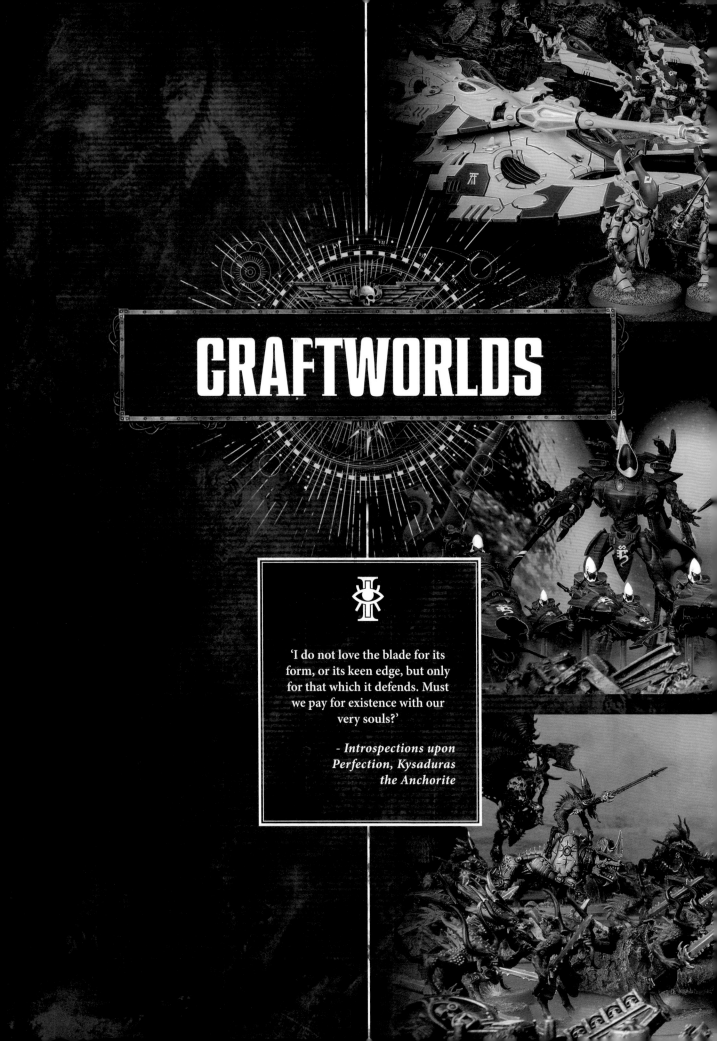

CRAFTWORLDS

'I do not love the blade for its form, or its keen edge, but only for that which it defends. Must we pay for existence with our very souls?'

- Introspections upon Perfection, Kysaduras the Anchorite

CHILDREN OF THE STARS

This section contains new and updated rules for *Codex: Craftworlds*, including revised datasheets, an Asuryani name generator, a range of Exarch powers, a new psychic discipline, and rules for creating custom Craftworld Attributes for your Craftworlds Detachments.

On the following pages you will find a name generator for Aeldari of the craftworlds, as well as the rules detailed below.

If your army is Battle-forged, certain rules found in this section – Powers of the Aspect Shrines, the Runes of Fortune, and Craftworld Attributes – can only be used to affect units within a Craftworlds Detachment (as defined in *Codex: Craftworlds*). Remember that a Detachment that includes any YNNARI unit – other than Yvraine, the Visarch, or the Yncarne – is not a Craftworlds Detachment.

UPDATED DATASHEETS

On pages 38-41, you will find background and updated datasheets for Jain Zar and Howling Banshees, designed to represent the latest iteration of these Citadel Miniatures.

Note that these datasheets, their wargear and the points values below update those found in the 2017 edition of *Codex: Craftworlds*, and should be used in your games of Warhammer 40,000.

POWERS OF THE ASPECT SHRINES

New powers for your Aspect Warrior Exarchs can be found on pages 42-46. These can be selected to replace certain abilities on each datasheet, or if you have a Battle-forged army, you can create Exarchs of legend by spending Command Points to add additional abilities.

RUNES OF FORTUNE

On page 47 you will find a new Psychic discipline for Asuryani psykers filled with new minor psychic powers which are easier to manifest.

CRAFTWORLD ATTRIBUTES

The last part of this section (pg 48-51) contains rules for creating your own Craftworld Attributes. These comprise a selection of abilities that can be combined to create a Battle-forged army ability that best represents the warriors of an Asuryani world-ship of your own devising, or one of the craftworlds in our publications that is not currently represented by a Craftworld Attribute.

POINTS VALUES

If you are playing a matched play game, or a game that uses a points limit, you can use the following list to determine the total points cost of your army. Simply add together the points of all your models to determine your army's total points value.

UNITS

UNIT	MODELS PER UNIT	POINTS PER MODEL (Including wargear)
Jain Zar	1	115

UNIT	MODELS PER UNIT	POINTS PER MODEL (Not including wargear)
Howling Banshees	5-10	9

OTHER WARGEAR

WARGEAR	POINTS PER ITEM
Banshee mask	0

RANGED WEAPONS

WEAPON	POINTS PER WEAPON
Shuriken pistol	0
Triskele	6

MELEE WEAPONS

WEAPON	POINTS PER WEAPON
Executioner	7
Mirrorswords	4
Power sword	4

ASURYANI NAME GENERATOR

Asuryani names are laden with nuance, subtle meanings and oblique references to allegory and myth, and are chosen as often as they are given. Some may change over a craftworlder's long life as they adopt new paths or earn epithets through exceptional deeds. If you wish to randomly generate a name for one of your Asuryani warriors, you can roll a D66 and consult the table below. To roll a D66, simply roll two D6, one after the other – the first represents tens, and the second represents digits, giving you a result between 11 and 66.

D66	FIRST ELEMENT	SECOND ELEMENT
11	Tenrith	the Fireheart
12	Justune	Kyldroth
13	Aleerith	Tridehlá
14	Yrlla	Who Walks Alone
15	Aileer	of the Flowing Spirits
16	Caslith	Iydoth
21	Tai'shar	Brylliel
22	Jair	Biel-rith
23	Luirth	(no second appellation)
24	Aleera	Iyadolath
25	Phyllistra	Last of the House of the Ayandi
26	Myrnoth	the Melancholy
31	Fyrram	Llacharni ('brightheart')
32	Ishylla	the Huntress
33	Tishriel	Aryimelli
34	Aydona	Bringer of Azure Death
35	Galánta	Umachuli
36	Ylleth	Shelwe-hann ('song of enlightenment')
41	Giladrea	Serenti ('glory of the setting sun')
42	Osinell	Ullamar
43	Glenoighi	Dystari ('that which will never shatter')
44	Ishtá	Ciaradh
45	Yvraine	Iyadari
46	Intrisiel	Flethál ('star-pattern of perfection')
51	Torc	the Whisper of Death
52	Anesh	Hanndroth ('quest eternal')
53	Kalistri	Sheersom
54	Alee	Cegodari ('who laughs at despair')
55	Altanish	Ullathani ('she who walks many paths')
56	Gwyth	Corsikanni ('kin to Corsairs')
61	Tyrelli	Yn Farwolloch ('deadly to her enemies')
62	Kaithe	Indomi
63	Galrethi	Saim-Ingrelli ('the grace of the striking snake')
64	Noithi	Ysbwrieli ('star-splinter')
65	Braesil	Morai-fen
66	Meari	Undomniel

ASURYANI NAME GENERATOR (MALE)

D66	FIRST ELEMENT	SECOND ELEMENT
11	Fachean	Son of Coheria
12	Tarvaril	Finarfin
13	Fánai	Eldrion
14	Yrmnoch	the Unyielding Fire
15	Barahir	Glaermril
16	Eldrion	Arronnás
21	Dis'ar	Gloywach ('the glow dragon')
22	Eldos	the Uncompromising
23	Kinshar	of the Noble House of Picarothi
24	Rhidhal	Enbrondil
25	Athairnos	Lladronoth
26	Eärandil	Bechareth ('spirit on the wind')
31	Siriolas	Ceifulgaithann ('wind rider')
32	Bahtaam	Undroíl
33	Fian	Caman ('the avenger')
34	Eldroth	Tóir
35	Lorinth	Scion of Rhidmar
36	Illisar	the Wanderer
41	Ealion	of the Clan Randras
42	Elronhir	Llmaea-fen ('born of black suns')
43	Tamishar	Rillietar
44	Arenal	Elarique of Alaitoc
45	Iradil	Sydarus Starstrider
46	Maur	the Implacable
51	Requiel	Ulthos ('speaker of unspeakable truths')
52	Lann	Sharnál
53	Yrule	the Deathly Eloquent
54	Ra'thar	Born of Twilight
55	Las'hár	of the Tower of Stars
56	Arision	Shelwe-nin ('song of the fading star')
61	Ingfhar	the Undaunted
62	Senn	Rhianthari ('starlight partially obscured by nebula')
63	Hal'thar	Eldroneth
64	Yrion	Trithjain ('storm of the stars')
65	Silgar	the Rising Star
66	Konrith	Bhanlhar ('avenger of the lost clan')

JAIN ZAR

THE STORM OF SILENCE

Regal and elegant in repose, yet a maelstrom of bladed violence when her wrath is unleashed, Jain Zar is the wrath of the Aeldari war god made manifest. A Phoenix Lord, she has lived and died countless times, every triumph an offering to Khaela Mensha Khaine and every death a martyrdom to the Asuryani cause.

First to learn under the great Asurmen's tutelage was Jain Zar, a passionate Aeldari swordmaiden famed for her lightning speed and ferocity. She and her brothers-in-arms learned well at the feet of their master, and in turn they assumed the mantle of the Asurya, spreading their own teachings across the stars and founding the shrines of the Warrior Aspects – shrines that Jain Zar still frequents to this day. Of all the Phoenix Lords, Jain Zar is the most devoted to the shrines of the Warrior Aspects, nurturing her spiritual descendants. Although she might disappear for centuries at a time, she always returns, and the shrines maintain a special vigil for her.

Jain Zar's astonishing swiftness and mercurial temperament are echoed by her Howling Banshee daughters, and it was she who first perfected the Scream that Steals – though the psychosonic barrage that emanates from her mask can not only stun foes, but liquefy their brains in the process. That death-dealing war cry has been heard across the galaxy, and it has proven that even the immortal servants of the Dark Gods are not above fear.

Jain Zar is the most active of all the Phoenix Lords in the war against the forces of the Great Enemy. She has led hundreds of Howling Banshees into battle on countless occasions, even mustering them from several craftworlds at once should she deem it necessary. Always at the forefront of a charge, she carries the Blade of Destruction, a long and elegantly balanced polearm originating from the distant past. Whirled in a bloody arc, the Blade of Destruction carves through the enemy, twirling to parry return blows before being used as leverage so Jain Zar can vault to a new position of advantage. With a flick of her wrist, the triskele known as the Silent Death is unleashed, a triple-bladed throwing weapon whose edges were forged in the ghostly flames of the warp. Black fire licks around the blade's edges as the Silent Death spins through the air in a graceful loop, leaving decapitated bodies in its wake before returning to its mistress. To watch Jain Zar in combat is to watch an exquisite dance that leaves even Harlequins agog; amidst leg sweeps, dodging twists and graceful pirouettes the glowing polearm scythes and darts until only the Phoenix Lord is left standing.

No other Phoenix Lord has championed the cause of the newly risen Ynnari as has Jain Zar. She has spoken with great force about the hope fostered by Ynnead, and come to the aid of Yvraine and her followers on multiple occasions since their first meeting aboard Biel-Tan.

JAIN ZAR

NAME	M	WS	BS	S	T	W	A	Ld	Sv
Jain Zar	8"	2+	2+	4	4	6	4	9	2+

Jain Zar is a single model equipped with: Silent Death; Blade of Destruction. You can only include one of this model in your army.

WEAPON	RANGE	TYPE	S	AP	D	ABILITIES
Silent Death	12"	Assault 4	User	-3	1	-
Blade of Destruction	Melee	Melee	+2	-3	D3	When resolving an attack made with this weapon, you can re-roll the wound roll.

ABILITIES	**Ancient Doom, Battle Focus** (see *Codex: Craftworlds*)	**Banshee Mask:** Enemy units cannot fire Overwatch at this model.

Acrobatic: This model can be chosen to charge with even if it Advanced this turn. If this model Advanced this turn, you can choose it to charge with if it is within 15" of any enemy units instead of 12", and you can add 3 to the charge roll.

The Storm of Silence: When this model fights, you can choose for its Attacks characteristic to be equal to the number of enemy models within 2" of it after any pile-in moves have been made.

Cry of War Unending: This model, and friendly **Howling Banshees** units that are within 6" of it at the start of the Fight phase, always fight first in the Fight phase, even if they did not charge. If the enemy has units that have charged, or that have a similar ability, then alternate choosing units to fight with, starting with the player whose turn is taking place.

War Shout: When resolving an attack made with a melee weapon against this model, subtract 1 from the hit roll.

FACTION KEYWORDS	**Aeldari, Asuryani, Aspect Warrior**
KEYWORDS	**Character, Infantry, Phoenix Lord, Jain Zar**

Jain Zar bounds ahead of warriors from Craftworld Biel-tan, racing to engage the enemies of the Aeldari.

HOWLING BANSHEES

Howling Banshees are swift and athletic Aspect Warriors who are famously deadly in melee. They embody the sudden wrath of Khaine, attacking with such swift certainty the foe has no time to properly defend itself. Using a special war mask to enhance their battle cries, they rob the wits of the enemy moments before the kill.

A predominantly female Aspect, what these fierce warriors lack in brute strength they more than make up for in precision and efficiency. While the foes reel from the auditory offensive of the banshee masks, the power swords of the Howling Banshees slice through the armour of their foes. Surrounded by a glimmering disruption field, these blades can carve through even ceramite. A Chaos Space Marine is as easily slain as a hulking Ork; haughty Incubi are as vulnerable as coarse and unsophisticated Imperial Guardsmen. Foes that turn to flee are ruthlessly pounced upon, or slashed to ribbons by razored projectiles from the Howling Banshees' shuriken pistols.

The banshee is a harbinger of woe in Aeldari mythology, whose cry is said to herald such ill fate it can even wrench a soul from its spirit stone. It is fitting that the most feared of all Aspect Warriors, the Howling Banshees, draw their

inspiration from this unearthly creature. In Aeldari myth, the Crone Goddess Morai-Heg sought to partake of the wisdom contained in her divine blood. Knowing there was only one with the power to harm a god, she sent her daughters to haunt their father Khaine's steps with their piercing screams. The infernal noise drove Khaine into a bloody rage that saw his mind unravel. Promising an end to the curse, the Crone Goddess bade Khaine cut off her hand that she might drink deep from her own veins. With this deed, Morai-Heg gained the knowledge of blood, and the Aspect of the Banshee was granted to Khaine in return.

The quintessential aspect of the banshee is weaponised via the banshee mask, a ritual piece of wargear containing psychosonic amplifiers that magnify the wearer's keening battle screams into a mind-destroying shock wave. This aural assault inflicts severe damage to the

central nervous system of their foes, inflicting a feeling of mortal terror and causing momentary paralysis even as the Howling Banshees dart in for the kill. A full squad of these Aspect Warriors activating their masks in unison can secure victory before a single blow is struck.

Howling Banshee Exarchs have surpassed their kin and given themselves over to their particular way of war entirely. It is they who pass on the teachings of Jain Zar. So piercing and shrill are the Exarch's own war cries that they haunt those who hear them even after the screams have died away, slowing down the enemy's reactions long after the initial paralysis wears off. Some Exarchs follow up their sonic assault with executioners, two-handed glaives that hit with devastating power. Others instead wield mirrorswords, reflective blades that are used to weave a whirling web of attacks that is all but impossible to evade.

HOWLING BANSHEES

NAME	M	WS	BS	S	T	W	A	Ld	Sv
Howling Banshee	8"	3+	3+	3	3	1	2	8	4+
Howling Banshee Exarch	8"	3+	3+	3	3	2	3	8	4+

This unit contains 5 Howling Banshees. It can include up to 5 additional Howling Banshees (**Power Rating +3**). A Howling Banshee Exarch can take the place of one Howling Banshee. Every model is equipped with: shuriken pistol; power sword. Every model has a banshee mask.

WEAPON	RANGE	TYPE	S	AP	D	ABILITIES
Shuriken pistol	12"	Pistol 1	4	0	1	When resolving an attack made with this weapon, on a wound roll of 6+ this weapon has an AP of -3 for that attack.
Triskele (shooting)	12"	Assault 3	4	-2	1	-
Executioner	Melee	Melee	+1	-3	D3	
Mirrorswords	Melee	Melee	User	-2	1	When resolving an attack made with this weapon, you can re-roll the hit roll.
Power sword	Melee	Melee	User	-3	1	-
Triskele (melee)	Melee	Melee	User	-2	1	-

WARGEAR OPTIONS	• The Howling Banshee Exarch can be equipped with one of the following instead of 1 power sword: 1 executioner; 1 triskele. • The Howling Banshee Exarch can be equipped with mirrorswords instead of 1 shuriken pistol and 1 power sword.

ABILITIES	**Ancient Doom, Battle Focus** (see *Codex: Craftworlds*) **Acrobatic:** This unit can be chosen to charge with even if it Advanced this turn. If this unit Advanced this turn, you can choose it to charge with if it is within 15" of any enemy units instead of 12", and you can add 3 to the charge roll.	**War Shout:** If this unit contains a Howling Banshee Exarch, then when resolving an attack made with a melee weapon against this unit, subtract 1 from the hit roll. **Banshee Mask:** Enemy units cannot fire Overwatch at this unit.

FACTION KEYWORDS	AELDARI, ASURYANI, ASPECT WARRIOR, <CRAFTWORLD>
KEYWORDS	INFANTRY, HOWLING BANSHEES

A squad of Howling Banshees surge from a Webway Gate with blades at the ready, the screeching of their masks heralding their foe's doom.

POWERS OF THE ASPECT SHRINES

The Exarchs of the Aspect Warrior shrines have long travelled the Path of the Warrior. Their skills honed over countless decades of war, they are amongst the finest fighters of the Asuryani.

Presented here are alternative abilities for the Exarchs from your Aspect Warrior units, allowing you to customise their datasheets and open up new strategies for using these peerless fighters on the battlefield. Alternatively, you can use the new Stratagems included in this section to grant additional abilities to your Exarchs, enabling you to represent the most truly devoted of Khaine's followers.

Note on your army roster any Exarch powers you have added or replaced for each Aspect Warrior unit in your army.

FIRE DRAGONS

The Fire Dragons burn with the heat of Vaul's own forge. Not only could Vaul craft fabulous devices but he could also melt down and destroy them; so it is with the Exarchs of the Fire Dragon shrines, who unleash powers of fiery unmaking upon living warrior and war engine alike.

If a **FIRE DRAGONS** unit from your army contains a Fire Dragon Exarch, you can replace the Crack Shot ability on that unit's datasheet with one of the Fire Dragon Exarch powers opposite. If you have any **FIRE DRAGONS** units in your army, you also have access to the Exemplar of the Dragon Shrine Stratagem below.

1CP

EXEMPLAR OF THE DRAGON SHRINE
Craftworlds Stratagem
This Exarch burns with inner fire and is surely a worthy inheritor of the armour of Fuegan.

Use this Stratagem before the battle. When you select a Fire Dragon Exarch power from the list opposite, you can take that ability in addition to the Crack Shot ability instead of replacing it. You can only use this Stratagem once per battle.

FIRE DRAGON EXARCH POWERS

Dragon's Bite: Whilst this unit contains a Fire Dragon Exarch, at the start of your Shooting phase you can change the Type characteristic of this unit's fusion guns to Pistol 1 until the end of that phase.

Tank Killer: When resolving an attack made with a firepike by this unit's Fire Dragon Exarch against a **VEHICLE** unit, you can re-roll one D6 when making the damage roll.

Burning Fists: Melee weapons that this unit's Fire Dragon Exarch is equipped with have an Armour Penetration characteristic of -2 and a Damage characteristic of 2. When resolving an attack made with a melee weapon by this unit's Fire Dragon Exarch, you can re-roll the wound roll.

Swiftstep: Whilst this unit contains a Fire Dragon Exarch, when this unit Advances you can roll three D6 and discard two of the results.

Wall of Fire: When this unit fires Overwatch, a Fire Dragon Exarch in this unit equipped with a Dragon's Breath Flamer can make a wall of fire attack. If he does so, instead of shooting with that model, roll one D6; on a 2+ the charging unit suffers D3 mortal wounds.

Burning Heat: Whilst this unit contains a Fire Dragon Exarch, when resolving an attack made with a melee weapon against this unit, subtract 1 from the hit roll.

DIRE AVENGERS

Devotees of Asuryan himself, those who walk the path of the Dire Avenger become adept at both attack and defence. Their Exarchs are masters of a swift and flexible warrior-stance that capitalises on everything it means to be Asuryani.

If a **DIRE AVENGERS** unit from your army contains a Dire Avenger Exarch, you can replace the Battle Fortune ability on that unit's datasheet with one of the Dire Avenger Exarch powers opposite. If you have any **DIRE AVENGER** units in your army, you also have access to the Exemplar of the Avenger Shrine Stratagem below.

1CP

EXEMPLAR OF THE AVENGER SHRINE
Craftworlds Stratagem

This Exarch possesses a deadly focus worthy of mighty Asuryan himself.

Use this Stratagem before the battle. When you select a Dire Avenger Exarch power from the list opposite, you can take that ability in addition to the Battle Fortune ability instead of replacing it. You can only use this Stratagem once per battle.

DIRE AVENGER EXARCH POWERS

Bladestorm: Whilst this unit contains a Dire Avenger Exarch, when resolving an attack made with a ranged weapon that does not have the Grenade type by a model in this unit, an unmodified hit roll of 6 scores 1 additional hit.

Defend: Whilst this unit contains a Dire Avenger Exarch, when resolving an attack made with a melee weapon against this unit, subtract 1 from the wound roll.

Stand Firm: Whilst this unit contains a Dire Avenger Exarch, when a Morale test is taken for this unit, do not roll the dice; it is automatically passed.

Martial Adept: This unit's Dire Avenger Exarch has a Weapons Skill and Ballistic Skill characteristic of 2+.

Shredding Fire: Ranged weapons that do not have the Grenade type that this unit's Dire Avenger Exarch is equipped with have an Armour Penetration characteristic of -3 and its Abilities text reads '-'.

Avenging Strikes: Whilst this unit contains a Dire Avenger Exarch and any models from this unit have been destroyed, when resolving an attack made by a model in this unit, add 1 to the hit roll and wound roll.

DARK REAPERS

Those who fight as Dark Reapers become living embodiments of death. Their Exarchs are anathema, grim and cruel-hearted figures whose every thought and deed are bent towards the annihilation of their foes by whatever means necessary. They are truly terrifying beings.

If a **DARK REAPER** unit from your army contains a Dark Reaper Exarch, you can replace the Crack Shot ability on that unit's datasheet with one of the Dark Reaper Exarch powers opposite. If you have any **DARK REAPER** units in your army, you also have access to the Exemplar of the Reaper Shrine Stratagem below.

1CP

EXEMPLAR OF THE REAPER SHRINE
Craftworlds Stratagem

This Exarch stands silently in battle, bringing a grim inevitability to his enemies' destruction.

Use this Stratagem before the battle. When you select a Dark Reaper Exarch power from the list opposite, you can take that ability in addition to the Crack Shot ability instead of replacing it. You can only use this Stratagem once per battle.

DARK REAPER EXARCH POWERS

Rapid Shot: When this unit's Dark Reaper Exarch shoots, add 1 to the number of attacks made with that model's ranged weapon.

Rain of Death: When this unit's Dark Reaper Exarch shoots with a tempest launcher, you can re-roll the dice to determine the number of attacks made.

Grim Visage: Whilst this unit contains a Dark Reaper Exarch, subtract 1 from the Leadership characteristic of enemy units whilst they are within 6" of this unit.

Long-ranged Fire: Whilst this unit contains a Dark Reaper Exarch, add 6" to the Range characteristic of ranged weapons models in this unit are equipped with.

Deadly Touch: When resolving an attack made with a melee weapon by this unit's Dark Reaper Exarch, an unmodified wound roll of 6 inflicts 2 mortal wounds on the target in addition to any other damage.

Focused Fire: When this unit is chosen to shoot with, this unit's Dark Reaper Exarch can target a **CHARACTER** unit even if it is not the closest enemy unit, so long as the target is within 18" of that Dark Reaper Exarch.

HOWLING BANSHEES

Speed, grace and overwhelming force are the hallmarks of the Howling Banshee shrines. Their Exarchs exhibit the greatest ability of all, their very presence enhancing the terrifying capacity for murder that their followers can unleash.

If a **HOWLING BANSHEES** unit from your army contains a Howling Banshee Exarch, you can replace the War Shout ability on that unit's datasheet with one of the Howling Banshee Exarch powers opposite. If you have any **HOWLING BANSHEE** units in your army, you also have access to the Exemplar of the Banshee Shrine Stratagem below.

HOWLING BANSHEE EXARCH POWERS

Graceful Avoidance: Whilst this unit contains a Howling Banshee Exarch, when a model in this unit would lose a wound in the Fight phase, roll one D6; on a 5+ that wound is not lost.

Piercing Strike: When this unit is chosen to fight with, a Howling Banshee Exarch in this unit that is equipped with an executioner can make a piercing strike. If they do, until the end of the phase, subtract 1 from the Attacks characteristic and add 3 to the Strength characteristic of that Howling Banshee Exarch, and that executioner has a Damage characteristic of 3.

Disarming Strike: At the start of the Fight phase, you can select one enemy model within 1" of this unit's Howling Banshee Exarch. Subtract 2 from the Attacks characteristic of that enemy model (to a minimum of 1) until the end of that phase.

Whirling Blades: Add 1 to the Attacks characteristic of this unit's Howling Banshee Exarch. If that Howling Banshee Exarch is equipped with mirrorswords, add 2 to its Attacks characteristic instead.

Decapitating Strikes: When resolving an attack made with a melee weapon by this unit's Howling Banshee Exarch, an unmodified hit roll of 6 inflicts 1 mortal wound on the target in addition to any normal damage.

Nerve-shredding Shriek: When this unit finishes a charge move, if it includes a Howling Banshee Exarch, you can select one enemy unit within 1" of this unit and roll one D6; on a 4+ that enemy unit suffers D3 mortal wounds.

1CP

EXEMPLAR OF THE BANSHEE SHRINE
Craftworlds Stratagem
The mournful wail of this Exarch has been the last thing heard by many foes of the Asuryani..

Use this Stratagem before the battle. When you select a Howling Banshee Exarch power from the list opposite, you can take that ability in addition to the War Shout ability instead of replacing it. You can only use this Stratagem once per battle.

SWOOPING HAWKS

Swooping Hawks rely upon speed and firepower to tear their foes apart, committing to melee only when they need to strike a killing blow. Their Exarchs perfectly embody this way of war.

If a **SWOOPING HAWKS** unit from your army contains a Swooping Hawks Exarch, you can replace the Herald of Victory ability on that unit's datasheet with one of the Swooping Hawk Exarch powers opposite. If you have any **SWOOPING HAWKS** units in your army, you also have access to the Exemplar of the Hawk Shrine Stratagem below.

SWOOPING HAWK EXARCH POWERS

Intercept: Whilst this unit contains a Swooping Hawk Exarch, when resolving an attack made by a model in this unit against an enemy unit that can **FLY**, you can re-roll the hit roll.

Suppressing Fire: When this unit's Swooping Hawk Exarch fires Overwatch at an enemy unit, subtract 2 from charge rolls made for that unit until the end of the phase.

Evade: Whilst this unit contains a Swooping Hawk Exarch, models in this unit have a 5+ invulnerable save.

Rapid Assault: If this unit made a charge move or was charged this turn, add 2 to the Attacks characteristic of this unit's Swooping Hawk Exarch this turn.

Fast Shot: Ranged weapons this unit's Swooping Hawk Exarch is equipped with have a Type characteristic of Assault 6.

Swooping Barrage: Whilst this unit contains a Swooping Hawk Exarch, add 1 to rolls made for this unit's Swooping Hawk Grenade Pack ability.

1CP

EXEMPLAR OF THE HAWK SHRINE
Craftworlds Stratagem
Gliding effortlessly above the battlefield, this Exarch leads their warriors in pinpoint strikes.

Use this Stratagem before the battle. When you select a Swooping Hawk Exarch power from the list opposite, you can take that ability in addition to the Herald of Victory ability instead of replacing it. You can only use this Stratagem once per battle.

STRIKING SCORPIONS

Striking Scorpions rely upon stealth to stalk their prey. When they attack, their Exarchs lead them in lightning-fast explosions of violence that see their foes reduced to torn and bloody shreds.

If a **STRIKING SCORPIONS** unit from your army contains a Striking Scorpions Exarch, you can replace the Sustained Attack ability on that unit's datasheet with one of the Striking Scorpion Exarch powers opposite. If you have any **STRIKING SCORPIONS** units in your army, you also have access to the Exemplar of the Scorpion Shrine Stratagem below.

1CP — EXEMPLAR OF THE SCORPION SHRINE
Craftworlds Stratagem

This Exarch is an expert hunter, remaining unseen by their foe until the moment they strike.

Use this Stratagem before the battle. When you select a Striking Scorpion Exarch power from the list opposite, you can take that ability in addition to the Sustained Attack ability instead of replacing it. You can only use this Stratagem once per battle.

STRIKING SCORPION EXARCH POWERS

Stalker: Whilst this unit contains a Striking Scorpion Exarch and is wholly on or within a terrain feature, when resolving an attack made with a ranged weapon against this unit, subtract 1 from the hit roll.

Crushing Blow: Add 2 to the Strength characteristic of this unit's Striking Scorpion Exarch.

Scorpion's Grasp: When resolving an attack made with a scorpion claw by this unit's Striking Scorpion Exarch, an unmodified hit roll of 6 inflicts 1 mortal wound on the target in addition to any normal damage.

Ambush: Whilst this unit contains a Striking Scorpion Exarch and is wholly on or within a terrain feature, this unit can always fight first in the Fight phase, even if they did not charge. If the enemy has units that have charged, or that have a similar ability, then alternate choosing units to fight with, starting with the player whose turn is taking place.

Withdraw: At the end of the Fight phase, if this unit contains a Striking Scorpion Exarch and is within 1" of any enemy models, this unit can make a Fall Back move of up to 6" as if it were your Movement phase.

Scorpion's Sting: Whilst this unit contains a Striking Scorpion Exarch, add 1 to rolls made for this unit's Mandiblasters ability.

SHINING SPEARS

Like elite cavalrymen, the Shining Spears fight from the saddles of their jetbike steeds with blistering speed and skill. So supremely graceful are their Exarchs that it is as though they ride the zephyrs of the wind themselves and strike with the fury of the hurricane.

If a **SHINING SPEARS** unit from your army contains a Shining Spear Exarch, you can replace the Expert Hunter ability on that unit's datasheet with one of the Shining Spear Exarch powers opposite. If you have any **SHINING SPEARS** units in your army, you also have access to the Exemplar of the Spear Shrine stratagem below.

1CP — EXEMPLAR OF THE SPEAR SHRINE
Craftworlds Stratagem

This Exarch manoeuvres their jetbike with breathtaking speed and skill.

Use this Stratagem before the battle. When you select a Shining Spear Exarch power from the list opposite, you can take that ability in addition to the Expert Hunter ability instead of replacing it. You can only use this Stratagem once per battle.

SHINING SPEAR EXARCH POWERS

Withdraw: At the end of the Fight phase, if this unit contains a Shining Spear Exarch and is within 1" of any enemy models, this unit can make a Fall Back move of up to 6" as if it were your Movement phase.

Swooping Dive: Whilst this unit contains a Shining Spear Exarch, when a charge roll is made for this unit, add 1 to the result.

Blademaster: A paragon sabre that this unit's Shining Spear Exarch is equipped with has a Damage characteristic of 3.

Lancer: When resolving an attack made with a laser lance or star lance by this unit's Shining Spear Exarch, an unmodified hit roll of 6 scores 1 additional hit.

Skilled Rider: This unit's Shining Spear Exarch has a 3+ invulnerable save against attacks made with ranged weapons.

Heartstrike: When resolving an attack made with a melee weapon by this unit's Shining Spear Exarch, an unmodified hit roll of 6 inflicts 1 mortal wound on the target in addition to any normal damage.

CRIMSON HUNTERS

Few, if any, can equal the airborne grace, skill and lethality of the Crimson Hunters. Their Exarchs are sufficiently deadly that they make even the ace pilots of the galaxy's other races look like fumbling green recruits.

If your army contains a **CRIMSON HUNTERS EXARCH**, you can replace the Marksman's Eye ability on that unit's datasheet with one of the Crimson Hunter Exarch powers opposite. If you have any **CRIMSON HUNTER EXARCH** units in your army, you also have access to the Exemplar of the Hunter Shrine Stratagem below.

EXEMPLAR OF THE HUNTER SHRINE
Craftworlds Stratagem
1CP

This Exarch slays their foes in dazzling feats of aerobatics before disappearing in a blur of crimson.

Use this Stratagem before the battle. When you select a Crimson Hunter Exarch power from the list opposite, you can take that ability in addition to the Marksman's Eye ability instead of replacing it. You can only use this Stratagem once per battle.

CRIMSON HUNTER EXARCH POWERS

Aerial Predator: When resolving an attack made with a ranged weapon by this model against a unit that can **FLY**, add 1 to the Damage characteristic of that weapon for that attack.

Evade: This unit has a 5+ invulnerable save.

Hawkeye: This model does not suffer the penalty for moving and firing Heavy weapons.

Strafing Assault: When resolving an attack made with a ranged weapon by this model against a unit that cannot **FLY**, re-roll a wound roll of 1.

Eyes of Khaine: When resolving an attack made with a ranged weapon by this model, the target does not receive the benefit of cover to its saving throw.

Aerial Manoeuvring: When this model moves, you can pivot it up to 180° before it moves, instead of up to 90°.

WARP SPIDERS

Warp Spider Exarchs are masters of misdirection. Their minds spin constantly with tactical ruses and vicious predatory schemes, made all the more deadly for their ability to think beyond the dull physical dimensions of realspace.

If a **WARP SPIDERS** unit from your army contains a Warp Spider Exarch, you can replace the Iron Resolve ability on that unit's datasheet with one of the Warp Spider Exarch powers opposite. If you have any **WARP SPIDERS** units in your army, you also have access to the Exemplar of the Spider Shrine Stratagem below.

EXEMPLAR OF THE SPIDER SHRINE
Craftworlds Stratagem
1CP

Flickering in and out of reality, this Exarch dissects their foes with pinpoint monofilament fire.

Use this Stratagem before the battle. When you select a Warp Spider Exarch power from the list opposite, you can take that ability in addition to the Iron Resolve ability instead of replacing it. You can only use this Stratagem once per battle.

WARP SPIDERS EXARCH POWERS

Surprise Assault: Whilst this unit contains a Warp Spider Exarch, when resolving an attack made with a death spinner by a model in this unit in a turn in which it was set up on the battlefield using the Warp Strike ability, you can re-roll the hit roll.

Withdraw: At the end of the Fight phase, if this unit contains a Warp Spider Exarch, this unit can make a Fall Back move of up to 6" as if it were your Movement phase.

Web of Deceit: Once per battle, in your Movement phase, if this unit contains a Warp Spider Exarch it can make a warp jump instead of moving normally. Remove this unit from the battlefield and set it up at the end of that phase, anywhere on the battlefield that is more than 9" away from any enemy models.

Spider's Lair: Whilst this unit contains a Warp Spider Exarch and is wholly on or within a terrain feature, when an enemy unit finishes a charge move within 1" of this unit, roll one D6; on a 3+ that enemy unit suffers D3 mortal wounds.

Flickering Assault: Whilst this unit contains a Warp Spider Exarch, models in this unit can pile in up to 6" instead of 3".

Spider's Bite: Powerblades this unit's Warp Spider Exarch is equipped with have a Strength characteristic of +1 and a Damage characteristic of 2.

RUNES OF FORTUNE

Those who walk the Path of the Seer can harness psychic energies to manifest a great many powers. Whilst their effects can be subtle, when applied at the correct moment, Aeldari lives may be saved and fate turned to a more favourable path.

Instead of knowing the *Smite* psychic power, <CRAFTWORLD> PSYKER models can instead know one of the psychic powers from the Runes of Fortune discipline. Before the battle, generate the psychic powers for <CRAFTWORLD> PSYKER models that know powers from the Runes of Fortune discipline using the table below. You can either roll one D6 to generate a power randomly, or you can select the power you wish each psyker to have.

D6 PSYCHIC POWER

1 FATEFUL DIVERGENCE

Exerting their will upon destiny, the psyker shifts the paths of fate.

Fateful Divergence has a warp charge value of 4. If manifested, select one friendly <CRAFTWORLD> unit within 6" of this psyker. Until the start of your next Psychic phase, you can re-roll a single hit roll, wound roll or save roll for that unit.

2 WITCH STRIKE

Focusing a still greater portion of their power into their weapon, each strike from the psyker blasts foes with potent aetheric energies.

Witch Strike has a warp charge value of 4. If manifested, until the start of your next Psychic phase, add 2 to the Damage characteristic of this psyker's melee weapons.

3 GHOSTWALK

Channelling energies from their runic armour, the psyker imbues their allies with ethereal speed.

Ghostwalk has a warp charge value of 6. If manifested, select one friendly <CRAFTWORLD> unit within 6" of this psyker. Until the start of your next Psychic phase, when a charge roll is made for that unit, add 2 to the result.

4 CRUSHING ORB

The psyker crushes their foe in a sphere of kinetic energy.

Crushing Orb has a warp charge value of 4. If manifested, select one enemy CHARACTER unit within 18" of and visible to this psyker, and roll three D6; for each roll of 5+ that CHARACTER unit suffers 1 mortal wound.

5 FOCUS WILL

The psyker channels their mind to aid a fellow seer.

Focus Will has a warp charge value of 6. If manifested, select one friendly <CRAFTWORLD> PSYKER model within 6" of this psyker. Until the end of this phase, when a Deny the Witch test is taken for that model, add 2 to the total.

6 IMPAIR SENSES

The psyker dims the foe's senses.

Impair Senses has a warp charge value of 6. If manifested, select one enemy unit within 18" of and visible to this psyker. Until the start of your next Psychic phase, when that unit is chosen to shoot with, models in that unit can only target the closest visible enemy unit unless the target of the attack is within 18" of the shooting model.

'The Dathedian's Curse, they call it. It brings nightmares, fathers lies and robs focus. Yet to those with the inner steel to harness it, it brings great strength. This I will prove to you on the morrow, when I write the doom of our foes in their own blood.'

- *High Warlock Iara, the Black Council of Altansar*

CRAFTWORLD ATTRIBUTES

Although their warrior cultures and practices can be traced back to the Aeldari empire of old, the craftworlds fight to preserve the last flickering embers of their dying race in their own distinct ways. These martial traditions are no less deadly for their differences, nor for the passing of millennia.

Codex: Craftworlds describes how the <CRAFTWORLD> keyword can be substituted with the name of your chosen craftworld, as well as describing the abilities that units in Craftworlds Detachments gain. One of these abilities is Craftworld Attributes. If your chosen craftworld does not have an associated Craftworld Attribute in Codex: Craftworlds, you can create its Craftworld Attribute by selecting rules from the list here. Unless otherwise stated, your chosen craftworld has two Craftworld Attributes from the following list:

Children of Khaine

This craftworld holds a special reverence for Khaine, and contains a great number of Aspect Shrines dedicated to the Bloody-handed God. The warriors these shrines produce are ruthless in the extreme, cutting down their enemies without mercy or hesitation.

When resolving an attack made with a melee weapon by an **ASPECT WARRIOR** model with this attribute, on an unmodified wound roll of 6 add 1 to the Damage characteristic of that weapon for that attack.

Children of Morai-Heg

The story of Morai-Heg teaches all Aeldari that wisdom cannot come without sacrifice. Some craftworlds even take the severed hand of Morai-Heg as their sigil, reminding them that in even the most dire circumstances, legends can be born.

When resolving an attack made by a model with this attribute in a unit in which at least half its starting number of models have been destroyed, add 1 to the hit roll. For the purposes of this attribute, destroyed models returned to a unit with this attribute are still considered to have been destroyed.

Children of Prophecy

A larger proportion of this craftworld's citizens find themselves drawn to the Path of the Seer. As a result, they can better focus and direct psychic energy in battle and know how best to avoid the dangers of those that hunger in the immaterium.

When a Psychic test is taken for a model with this attribute, each individual dice roll of 1 is treated as a 2.

Children of the Open Skies

These Aeldari display an affinity for open spaces, the vast training domes of their craftworld perfect for honing the skills of their Windriders and other airborne warriors.

When a unit with this attribute that can **FLY** Advances, add an additional 2" to the Move characteristics of models in that unit until the end of the phase.

Diviners of Fate

The Farseers of this craftworld share openly the twists of fate they have seen. Each warrior goes to battle knowing a portion of what awaits them, allowing them to anticipate and avoid situations that might otherwise see them slain.

Models with this attribute have a 6+ invulnerable save.

Expert Crafters

Some Aeldari display an affinity for crafting wraithbone into beautiful sculptures that bring tears to the eyes of connoisseurs. They can also turn this art towards creating potent weapons of war.

When a unit with this attribute fires Overwatch or is chosen to shoot or fight with, you can re-roll a single hit roll and you can re-roll a single wound roll.

Grim

The Aeldari of this craftworld have been to the forbidden places of the galaxy and triumphed against its many horrors. For them the darkness holds no fear, for they have faced such dire situations before and emerged victorious.

When a Morale test is taken for a unit with this attribute, you can re-roll the dice.

Hail of Doom

When gathered in large numbers, the focused shuriken-fire of the Asuryani falls upon the foe like a rain of blades. Even the toughest plate is slashed to ribbons by the hail of deadly projectiles.

When resolving an attack made with a shuriken weapon by a model with this attribute against an enemy unit within 12" of that model, improve the Armour Penetration characteristic of that weapon by 1 (e.g. AP 0 becomes AP -1). This does not affect the abilities of that shuriken weapon (i.e. a wound roll of 6+ is still resolved at AP-3).

A shuriken weapon is any weapon whose profile includes the word 'shuriken' (shuriken pistol, Avenger shuriken catapult etc.), a scorpion's claw (shooting) and any Relic that replaces a shuriken weapon (e.g. Kurnous' Bow).

Headstrong

When the call of war is sent out and the fury of Khaine pumps through their veins, these Aeldari can barely contain their need to get to grips with their foes and destroy them.

When a charge roll is made for a unit with this attribute, add 1 to the result.

Hunters of Ancient Relics

All Aeldari seek out relics from the glorious past, when their race was at its zenith and artefacts of great power were created throughout their empire. Since the Fall, many of these have been lost, but there are some who see these priceless treasures as the key to their race's survival, and will fight all the harder to recover them.

Add 1 to the Attacks characteristic of models with this attribute whilst their unit is within 3" of any objective markers.

Martial Citizenry

Many craftworlds train even their ordinary citizenry to the same degree as the professional soldiers of other races.

When resolving an attack made by a **Guardian** model with this attribute, re-roll a hit roll of 1.

Masterful Shots

The warriors of this craftworld have trained long at fighting their wars in dense terrain. To give them even the merest glimpse of yourself is to invite death.

When resolving an attack made by a model with this attribute, the target does not receive the benefit of cover to its saving throw.

Masters of Concealment

Turning their talents to self-preservation, and utilising complex camouflage fields, the warriors of this craftworld turn every scrap of cover to their advantage.

When resolving an attack made with a ranged weapon against a unit with this attribute by a model that is more than 12" away, that unit is treated as having the benefit of cover to its saving throw.

Mobile Fighters

These warriors have trained extensively with the grav-tank pilots of their craftworld. In the blink of an eye, their transports will descend, disgorging warriors who spit deadly accurate salvoes of fire or plunge blades-first into their stunned foes before they can react.

When resolving an attack made by a model with this attribute in a turn in which that model's unit disembarked from a transport, re-roll a hit roll of 1.

Savage Blades

Whilst many craftworlds do not encourage their warriors to put themselves in harm's way, others positively encourage their fighters to destroy their enemies blade to blade.

When resolving an attack made with a melee weapon by a model with this attribute in a turn in which that model's unit made a charge move, was charged or performed a Heroic Intervention, re-roll a hit roll of 1.

Strike and Fade

The inhabitants of this craftworld can claim a mastery of hit and run tactics beyond that normally displayed by their cousins.

If you select this Craftworld Attribute you cannot select a second. Units with this attribute can Charge during a turn in which they Fell Back. When a model with this attribute that is not within 3" of any enemy units makes a consolidation move, it does not have to end that move closer to the nearest enemy model.

Students of Vaul

Some craftworlds utilise wraithbone vehicle hulls infused with additional empathic circuits. When attacked, the pilot can divert a portion of their consciousness to repairing and regrowing the most serious damage, allowing them to fight at peak efficiency long enough to see victory won.

At the start of your turn, each **Vehicle** model with this attribute regains 1 lost wound.

Superior Shurikens

Utilising more aerodynamic shurikens, superior gravitic accelerators or potent trajectory calculators, the warriors of this craftworld are able to project shurikens over greater distance.

Add 4" to the Range characteristic of shuriken weapons models with this attribute are equipped with.

A shuriken weapon is any weapon whose profile includes the word 'shuriken' (shuriken pistol, Avenger shuriken catapult etc.), a scorpion's claw (shooting) and any Relic that replaces a shuriken weapon (e.g. Kurnous' Bow).

Vengeful Blades

Whilst all craftworlds recognise the dire threat of Slaanesh, many also recognise that She Who Thirsts is but one piece of a greater threat to the galaxy. The warriors of these world-ships are indiscriminate in opposing the threat of Chaos and treat the minions of all the gods with equal ire.

When resolving an attack made with a melee weapon by a model with this attribute against a **Chaos** unit in a turn in which that model's unit made a charge move, was charged, or performed a Heroic Intervention, you can re-roll the hit roll.

Warding Runes

These warriors decorate their armour and wargear with ancient Aeldari runes of warding. Malign energies that would slay these warriors are mysteriously turned aside.

When a model with this attribute would lose a wound as a result of a mortal wound, roll one D6; on a 5+ that wound is not lost.

Webway Warriors

The warriors of this craftworld know many of the secret paths of the webway, and can use them to launch devastating ambushes on their foes.

The Webway Strike Stratagem (see *Codex: Craftworlds*) can be used one additional time per battle for each Detachment (excluding Auxiliary Support Detachments) in your army that contains units with this attribute. The second and any subsequent uses of this Stratagem can only be used to set up units with this attribute in the webway.

Wrath of the Dead

Most Aeldari find the use of ghost warriors to be distasteful, but sometimes the dead don't rest easy and are eager to vent their fury at the living.

When resolving an attack made by a **Wraith Construct** with this attribute, re-roll a wound roll of 1.

'We Aeldari are being tested, as the blade Asha'qui was tested beneath Vaul's anvil. Will we break? I think not. From this time of psychic trauma, we will emerge stronger than ever before.'

- Yvraine, Daughter of Shades and High Priestess of Ynnead

DRUKHARI

'The Imperium Nihilus has been
plunged into darkness. Now
more than ever, the wretched
Drukhari are emerging from
their lairs, thirsting to prey on
the fearful and the weak. We
alone can hurl them back!'

*- Captain Erasmus Threnn of
Ventrillia (deceased)*

DENIZENS OF THE DARK CITY

This section contains new and updated rules for *Codex: Drukhari*, including revised datasheets, a Drukhari name generator, and rules for creating custom Kabal, Wych Cult and Haemonculus Coven Obsessions for your DRUKHARI Detachments.

On the following pages you will find a name generator for the Aeldari denizens of the Dark City, as well as the rules detailed below.

UPDATED DATASHEETS

On pages 56-59, you will find background and updated datasheets for Drazhar and Incubi, designed to represent the latest iteration of these Citadel Miniatures.

Note that these datasheets, their wargear and the points values below update those found in the 2018 edition of *Codex: Drukhari*, and should be used in your games of Warhammer 40,000.

DRUKHARI OBSESSIONS

The last part of this section contains rules for creating your own Drukhari Obsessions. This includes Kabal Obsessions (pg 61), Wych Cult Obsessions (pg 62) and Haemonculus Coven Obsessions (pg 63). Each of these comprises a selection of abilities that can be combined to create a Battle-forged army ability that best represents the forces of your custom Kabal, Wych Cult or Haemonculus Coven, or can be used to represent such a sub-faction found in the background of our publications that is not currently represented by a Drukhari Obsession.

POINTS VALUES

If you are playing a matched play game, or a game that uses a points limit, you can use the following list to determine the total points cost of your army. Simply add together the points of all your models to determine your army's total points value.

UNITS		
UNIT	MODELS PER UNIT	POINTS PER MODEL (Including wargear)
Drazhar	1	120
UNIT	MODELS PER UNIT	POINTS PER MODEL (Not including wargear)
Incubi	5-10	16

MELEE WEAPONS	
WEAPON	POINTS PER WEAPON
Demiklaives	0
Klaive	0

DRUKHARI NAME GENERATOR

Pureblood Drukhari offspring are given names that proclaim the arrogant and elite lineage of their parents. By comparison those that are grown must claim or make their own names, ensuring through violence and bloodshed that they are known and respected throughout the Dark City. If you wish to randomly generate a name for one of your Drukhari warriors, you can roll a D66 and consult the table below. To roll a D66, simply roll two D6, one after the other – the first represents tens, and the second represents digits, giving you a result between 11 and 66.

KABALITE NAME GENERATOR

D66	TAKEN NAME	KABALITE NAME
11	Anarkyss	Sar'sel
12	Veth'va	Vorpex
13	Mayator	Kreen
14	Quaez	the Bloodbreather
15	Daisan	Maestros
16	Bekliel	Gaarsus
21	Orvak	Ehthrek
22	Narlek	Ghorghast
23	Monsatos	Ignyss
24	Vivithrax	Mohrkhar
25	Drevakh	Thresk
26	Kyzarkh	Scaur
31	Thresyn	the Pale
32	Shylas	Khadylus
33	Lythric	Phrel
34	Kylos	Vulkyriax
35	Theskril	Nul
36	Skythe	the Flenser
41	Akkhar	Poisonblade
42	Kharsac	Barbtongue
43	Nyktos	Xesh
44	Grevyth	the Ravening
45	Thraed	Draeven
46	Sykil	of the Obsidian Needle
51	Khaeyl	Vhrex
52	Madrax	Kaghmyr
53	Akhirion	Thrail
54	Vypus	Flickerblade
55	Ethriliac	Xosh
56	Kheraes	the Bleak
61	Iyshak	Neverbreath
62	Khepres	Skahyl
63	Eldoriac	Verkosian
64	Vrekkus	Ulthurian
65	Thayd	Menesh
66	Xurul	the Cruel

WYCH CULT NAME GENERATOR

D66	TAKEN NAME	CULT NAME
11	Ariex	La'flenz
12	Melikka	Wysp
13	Grendett	Soriel
14	Vaivel	Oblique
15	Bithandrel	Nervose
16	Ingenue	Mourn
21	Demadyne	Vivicon
22	Laelanyel	Viserhyx
23	Excrucia	Berrebaal
24	Nathra	Vulptuse
25	Vrexith	Ehlynna
26	Thyndrella	Khaur
31	Selithrian	Hexehss
32	Xela	the Crimson
33	Peiythia	Thrix
34	Uless	Khoryssa
35	Skyshrin	Vexx
36	Anielyn	of the Screaming Blade
41	Vyrenik	Khrygg
42	Khatryx	Nichtren
43	Nyssa	Veluxis
44	Phyrix	the Huntress
45	Mellyx	Beastbane
46	Kherissa	the Magnificent
51	Tryxin	Trehll
52	Aniellah	Xyriphraxis
53	Veshtari	Masdruvael
54	Morghynn	Khrone
55	Thrixxesh	the Untouched
56	Thessa	Bloodslyk
61	Xindrell	the Cruel
62	Kladys	Kharavyxis
63	Shemriel	Ynthrekh
64	Lyxanna	Dyvahur
65	Nimhre	Krael
66	Vylekh	the Bloodsister

HAEMONCULUS COVEN NAME GENERATOR

D66	TAKEN NAME	COVEN NAME
11	Makaxev	Ghassuhr
12	Dhyzn	Enagathri
13	Silyasq	Venas-Thryn
14	Vralpl	Zhodt
15	Archdeacon	Anachroi
16	Yukor	Illathrian
21	Zancathryx	the Black Scalpel
22	Vynquiliac	Xorl
23	Qualaria	Sslyth-Taker
24	Haemogarch	Vanthis
25	Shegmeth	Kro
26	Khaebris	Xulfur
31	Gnesu	Ilynneadh
32	Nothraq	Gnull
33	Viscount	Syndriq
34	Quvelich	the Emaciator
35	Maestru	Thrylemnis
36	Lord	Faerughast
41	Croniarch	Sekh
42	Iridivyst	the Gourmet
43	Xeryndtuil	the Apotheosor
44	Synistrid	Assp
45	Ghyllzeth	the Bleak
46	Zhervyu	Mala-Glissande
51	Immile	Tzantuathrelle
52	Diablythe	the Last Touch
53	Tshein-gu	Fingersnap
54	Kresthekia	Carna-Thryss
55	Ex-Acothyst	Mydilian
56	Ymodrian	Gruelle
61	Quarandtor	of Many Smiles
62	Maultarque	Oslarielle
63	Divine Lady	Cronestalker
64	Unctuo	Xarathrullien
65	Doshvhar	of Few Mercies
66	Endtru	Zanandor

DRAZHAR

MASTER OF BLADES

The warrior known as Drazhar speaks only with his weapons. With exquisite skill his demiklaives flash out, clasped as one single greatblade one moment and dancing as two perfectly balanced swords the next. Like a serpent he weaves through the enemy ranks, arcs of bright blood trailing like streamers behind him.

Even amongst the ranks of the secretive Incubi, Drazhar remains a mystery. All that is known of his origins is that he entered the Great Shrine of the Incubi unannounced and unbidden, clad in the segmented armour of the Incubus creed. The subsequent leadership duel with the incumbent Hierarch was over within minutes. Drazhar stepped over the Hierarch's dismembered body before sketching a simple bow, thereafter taking the position of the sacred executioner of his order – lethality personified.

Drazhar's mysterious appearance gave rise to many wild theories and unanswered questions. Some say he is Arhra, the fabled Dark Father of the Incubi incarnate, others that his armour is filled with nothing more than bone-dust. Though he has become an integral part of the Great Shrine since his dramatic appearance, he has famously never spoken, nor removed his helmet,

not even to eat or sleep. Even the name Drazhar is ceremonial, meaning 'living sword.' The most that can be expected by way of conversation is an occasional slight nod or tilt of the head, and it is only the most senior Incubi who are accorded even this scant courtesy. The lords of other Incubi shrines treat the Master of Blades with extreme suspicion, for despite their revered position each was once a lesser warrior, flawed and mortal. Drazhar alone remains incorruptible by emotion or pride. He simply exists to kill – nothing more, nothing less.

Every strike of Drazhar's demiklaives exemplifies the merciless tenets of his order, every life he claims a gruesome liturgy for his dark brethren. Taller and more lithe than even other Incubi, Drazhar has a deadly, mantis-like speed. He has an uncanny ability to move through even the most chaotic

melee like lightning, cutting down his chosen victims before their blades can fall or their trigger fingers can twitch. Those chosen as his prey have only seconds left to live.

Drazhar is one of very few Commorrites who is widely admired within the Dark City. The deeds of this enigmatic bladesman are often spoken about, particularly by those Drukhari who managed to secure his services on a realspace raid. There are countless stories of his macabre work that have spread from Commorragh to the webway and even the craftworlds, such as the time he personally butchered every Imperial defender in the tallest spire of Hive Tarson, or when he single-handedly despatched a trio of Custodian Guard at close quarters. Should he cement his pre-eminence as Commorragh's finest bladesman by slaying a Phoenix Lord in a duel, his legend would resound across eternity.

DRAZHAR

NAME	M	WS	BS	S	T	W	A	Ld	Sv
Drazhar	7"	2+	2+	4	4	6	4	9	2+

Drazhar is a single model equipped with: The Executioner's Demiklaives. You can only include one of this model in your army.

WEAPON	RANGE	TYPE	S	AP	D	ABILITIES
The Executioner's Demiklaives	When the bearer fights, select one of the profiles below.					
- Single blade	Melee	Melee	+1	-3	2	-
- Dual blades	Melee	Melee	User	-2	2	When the bearer fights with dual blades, it can make 2 additional attacks with this weapon.

ABILITIES		
	Power From Pain (see *Codex: Drukhari*)	**Eternal Warrior:** This model has a 5+ invulnerable save.
	Murderous Assault: If this model made a charge move this turn, you can choose to fight with this model an additional time this turn.	**Tormentors:** When a Morale test is taken for an enemy unit within 6" of any **Incubi** units from your army, and the result of that Morale test is equal to the highest Leadership characteristic in that enemy unit, the test is failed and one model flees that enemy unit.
	Lethal Precision: When resolving an attack made with a melee weapon by this model, on an unmodified wound roll of 6 add 2 to the Damage characteristic of that weapon for that attack.	**Master of Blades:** Add 1 to wound rolls for friendly **Incubi** units whilst they are within 6" of this model.

FACTION KEYWORDS	**AELDARI, DRUKHARI, INCUBI**
KEYWORDS	**CHARACTER, INFANTRY, DRAZHAR**

Under dark skies filled with vicious Drukhari aircraft, Drazhar leads his Incubi in the attack.

INCUBI

The Incubi are an order devoted to the merciless kill. No sense of honour stays their blades, no trick or misdirection is considered taboo. They even use the tortured spirit stones of dead Aeldari to deliver a pulse of mind-numbing anguish as they fight, making them all the more deadly at close quarters.

The Incubi are an order of Drukhari that have honed themselves for war and war alone. Warriors of the highest calibre, they dedicate themselves to the perfection of the killing strike. Incubi exist apart from the norm of Commorrite society; in fact, they take pains to do so. Instead of taking pleasure where they can find it and indulging their every whim like normal inhabitants of the Dark City, Incubi lead rigorously disciplined lives that include all manner of aberrations, such as self-denial and delayed gratification. It is said that alone amongst the Drukhari the Incubi can be trusted to keep their word. Not only that, but when they put an end to their victims' lives, they do so not over a period of time so as to savour the kill, but with a swift severing blow.

Most Incubi begin their tenure as veteran warriors that have grown obsessed with the act of the 'perfect kill'. The best way to ensure plenty of opportunities for violent death is to enter one of the Incubi shrines as a supplicant to Khaine, the Bloody-Handed God, for the Incubi are constantly in demand as mercenaries and realspace raiders. Should the aspirant manage to enter the shrine alive, all previous concerns from his former life are put aside, and his already impressive martial skills are honed until they become preternaturally advanced. Only once an aspirant has managed to best a proven Incubus and donned his armour will he be accepted as an initiate. Still his transformation is not complete. Only when the initiate has killed an Aspect Warrior of the craftworlds and taken his shattered spirit stone – later to be remade into an arcane device called a tormentor – will he be properly inducted into the ranks of his brethren.

Everything about a fully armoured Incubus conveys a message of violent death. His armour is spiked and segmented from top to toe, and his helm, horned in the manner of a Daemon, is framed by a pair of great razored blades. He walks with the measured surety of a stalking sabrecat, and despite his formidable armour he makes no sound as he does so, for each bodysuit is so perfectly designed it barely inhibits his dexterity.

Though they train in almost every form of blade, the Incubi favour large, powered swords they call klaives. Klaives are considered to be the one true weapon, for each is a masterpiece of balance and form. A Klaivex – the leader of each Incubi wargroup – may favour ritual variants such as demiklaives and switchklaives. Being Drukhari, the Incubi do not hesitate to tip the scales in their favour. When they close upon their foe they activate their tormentors – these arcane constructions send intense waves of anguish and despair straight into the minds of their intended prey.

INCUBI

NAME	M	WS	BS	S	T	W	A	Ld	Sv
Incubus	7"	3+	3+	3	3	1	3	8	3+
Klaivex	7"	2+	3+	3	3	2	4	9	3+

This unit contains 1 Klaivex and 4 Incubi. It can include up to 5 additional Incubi (**Power Rating +4**). Each model is equipped with: klaive.

WEAPON	RANGE	TYPE	S	AP	D	ABILITIES
Demiklaives	When the bearer fights, select one of the profiles below.					
- Single blade	Melee	Melee	+1	-3	1	-
- Dual blades	Melee	Melee	User	-2	1	When the bearer fights with dual blades, it can make 2 additional attacks with this weapon.
Klaive	Melee	Melee	+1	-3	1	-

WARGEAR OPTIONS	• The Klaivex can be equipped with demiklaives instead of 1 klaive.

ABILITIES	**Power From Pain** (see *Codex: Drukhari*) **Lethal Precision:** When resolving an attack made with a melee weapon by a model in this unit, on an unmodified wound roll of 6 add 2 to the Damage characteristic of that weapon for that attack.	**Tormentors:** When a Morale test is taken for an enemy unit within 6" of any **INCUBI** units from your army, and the result of that Morale test is equal to the highest Leadership characteristic in that enemy unit, the test is failed and one model flees that enemy unit.

FACTION KEYWORDS	AELDARI, DRUKHARI, INCUBI

KEYWORDS	INFANTRY

Out of the gloom the Incubi strike, wicked klaives ready to dismember and disembowel.

DRUKHARI OBSESSIONS

There are a great many groups vying for power in the labyrinthine nightmare realm of Commorragh. Each of these has their own particular preferences and practices when it comes to raiding realspace and feeding on the pain and terror of their prey.

Codex: Drukhari describes how the <**Kabal**>, <**Wych Cult**> and <**Haemonculus Coven**> keywords can be substituted with the name of your chosen Kabal, Wych Cult and Haemonculus Coven, as well as describing the abilities that units in **Drukhari** Detachments gain. One of these abilities is Drukhari Obsessions. If your chosen Kabal, Wych Cult or Haemonculus Coven does not have an associated obsession in *Codex: Drukhari*, you can create its Drukhari Obsession by selecting rules from the Kabal Obsessions (see opposite), Wych Cult Obsessions (pg 62) or Haemonculus Coven Obsessions (pg 63) lists respectively. Unless otherwise stated, your chosen Kabal, Wych Cult or Haemonculus Coven has two Drukhari Obsessions from the relevant list.

If your army is Battle-forged, these rules can only be used to affect units within a **Drukhari** Detachment (as defined in *Codex: Drukhari*). Remember that a Detachment that includes any **Ynnari** unit – other than Yvraine, the Visarch, or the Yncarne – is not a **Drukhari** Detachment.

'There are as many subcultures in Commorragh's vast sprawl as there are vermin swimming in the River Khaïdes that flows beneath it. Each clique and stratum has its own predilections, but one thing they share without exception – a grotesque thirst for acts of death and bloodshed.'

- Inquisitor Hakoa Temenu of the Ordo Xenos

KABAL OBSESSIONS

Dark Mirth

This Kabal revels in the misfortunes of others. From driving panicking victims into minefields to seeing proud fighters flee in terror, the sinister chuckling of these warriors is often the last thing their victims hear.

Subtract 1 from the Leadership characteristic of enemy units whilst they are within 6" of any units from your army with this obsession. The first time an enemy unit fails a Morale test in a battle, add 1 to the Leadership characteristic of models from your army with this obsession until the end of that battle.

Deadly Deceivers

Cruel misdirection is this Kabal's speciality, whether that is seeding the ground before them with torment mines, a feigned retreat leading the foe into an ambush or disappearing from view only to plunge their blade into an enemy's back.

Units with this obsession can charge in a turn in which they Fell Back. When an enemy unit finishes a charge move within 1" of any units with this obsession, roll one D6; on a 6, that enemy unit suffers 1 mortal wound.

Disdain for Lesser Beings

This Kabal inhabits some of the highest spires of Commorragh, allowing them to literally look down on their rivals. Convinced of their superiority, these haughty warriors see victory as an absolute certainty, and to flee before their lessers is all but unthinkable.

When a Morale test is taken for a unit with this obsession, no more than one model can flee.

Meticulous Flayers

This Kabal has turned the act of flaying their foes into an art form. A few well-placed slices are all they need to remove the majority of their victim's skin before they die in excruciating agony.

Units with this obsession that have the Power From Pain ability always benefit from the Eager to Flay bonus (see *Codex: Drukhari*), even during the first battle round. When resolving an attack made with a melee weapon by a model with this obsession against a unit that is not a **VEHICLE** or **TITANIC**, an unmodified hit roll of 6 automatically scores a hit and successfully wounds the target (do not make a wound roll).

Mobile Raiders

This Kabal revels in high-speed warfare, riding superior grav-craft to battle so as to ensure they reach the foe before their erstwhile allies do. It is said that even the Reaver gangs of Commorragh are envious of the swiftness of this Kabal's craft.

Add 3" to the Move characteristic of models with this obsession that can **FLY**.

Soul Bound

This Kabal has studied the process of dying for countless centuries, experimenting with binding souls to corpses in the hopes of mastering the transition between life and death.

When an Inured to Suffering roll is made for a model with this obsession, re-roll a roll of 1. Units with this obsession that do not have the Power From Pain ability instead gain the Inured to Suffering bonus (see *Codex: Drukhari*).

Toxin Crafters

This Kabal is a manufacturer and distributor of many lethal poisons, but they are careful to always maintain a large stockpile of their most potent toxins for their own nefarious use.

When resolving an attack made with a poisoned weapon by a model with this obsession, on an unmodified wound roll of 6 add 1 to the Damage characteristic of that weapon for that attack. This does not apply to Artefacts of Cruelty. For the purposes of this obsession, a poisoned weapon is any weapon that has the Poisoned Weapon ability (see *Codex: Drukhari*).

Webway Raiders

The warriors of this Kabal are experts at using multiple webway portals to appear from unexpected quarters. Their enemies find themselves suddenly beset on all sides by swift and deadly fighters.

The Webway Portal Stratagem (see *Codex: Drukhari*) can be used one additional time per battle for each Detachment (excluding Auxiliary Support Detachments) in your army that contains units with this obsession. The second and any subsequent uses of this Stratagem can only be used to set up units with this obsession in the webway.

WYCH CULT OBSESSIONS

Acrobatic Display

This cult favours spectacular gymnastic displays. Its fighters are never still, springing from one foot to the other and flipping over the blows of their foe with ease.

If you select this Wych Cult Obsession you cannot select a second. Whilst a model with this obsession that has an invulnerable save is within 1" of any enemy units, improve its invulnerable save by 1, to a maximum of 3+ (e.g. a 4+ invulnerable save becomes a 3+). Whilst a model with this obsession that does not have an invulnerable save is within 1" of any enemy units, it has a 6+ invulnerable save.

The Art of Pain

Some Wych Cults elevate gladiatorial battles to another level, creating a spectacle that maims and cripples in order to draw out the moment of the kill, maximising the moment of suffering to heighten the pleasure they derive before the final blade falls.

Whilst units with this obsession that have the Power From Pain ability (see *Codex: Drukhari*) are within 1" of any enemy units, they treat the current battle round as being 1 higher than it actually is when determining what bonuses they gain from that ability.

Berserk Fugue

This cult's warriors enter a killing trance when the moment of combat is joined, ripping their foes apart in a flurry of blows that owes nothing to grace and everything to bestial fury.

When resolving an attack made with a melee weapon by a model with this obsession that made a charge move, was charged or performed a Heroic Intervention this turn, an unmodified hit roll of 6 scores 1 additional hit. You cannot select this obsession if you have already selected the Precise Killers obsession.

Precise Killers

This Wych Cult is known for the meticulous skill of its warriors. Even the thickest armour is no defence against their assault, as blades plunge through eye lenses and slice through vulnerable seams.

When resolving an attack made with a melee weapon by a model with this obsession, on an unmodified wound roll of 6 improve the Armour Penetration characteristic of that weapon by 1 for that attack (e.g. AP 0 becomes AP -1). You cannot select this obsession if you have already selected the Berserk Fugue obsession.

Slashing Impact

The warriors of this Wych Cult are adept at using their bladed armour and equipment as they plunge into the foe to open up veins and slash throats.

After a model with this obsession finishes a charge move, you can select one enemy **INFANTRY**, **BIKER** or **MONSTER** unit within 1" of it and roll one D6; on a 5+ that enemy unit suffers 1 mortal wound.

Stimulant Innovators

Not for this cult the banal stimulants of their peers. Its fighters believe in trying ever-more interesting and dangerous concoctions to fuel their displays. From Ambull adrena-gland distillations to pheromonic infusions derived from the Ethereals of the T'au, these warriors will try anything to give themselves an edge over their opponent, the potential for metabolic meltdown only adding to the thrill.

When the Hyperstimm Backlash Stratagem (see *Codex: Drukhari*) is used on a unit with this obsession, it only costs 1 Command Point instead of 2.

Test of Skill

This Wych Cult is driven to test its blade-craft against the largest and most dangerous foes in the galaxy. They are easily bored by slaughtering lesser foes, but when faced with a truly monstrous foe they attack and dismember it with surprising speed and delight.

When resolving an attack made by a model with this obsession against a **MONSTER** or **VEHICLE** unit in which any models have a Wounds characteristic of 10 or more, add 1 to the wound roll.

Trophy Takers

Taking a token from each defeated foe, the members of this cult are bedecked in patches of flayed skin, bones and skulls that proclaim their many victories.

When your opponent takes a Morale test for a unit in which any models were destroyed as a result of an attack made with a melee weapon by a model with this obsession this turn, they must roll two D6 and discard the lowest result. If both results are the same, discard either of them.

HAEMONCULUS COVEN OBSESSIONS

Artists of the Flesh

The masters of this Coven are true masters of this craft, the products of their depraved surgeries emerging tougher and more resilient than those of their rivals.

If you select this Haemonculus Coven Obsession you cannot select a second. When resolving an attack against a unit with this Obsession, subtract 1 from the Damage characteristic of the weapon making that attack (to a minimum of 1).

Dark Harvest

This Coven waits with the patience of a spider, before descending on their victims in great force to gather a harvest of terror and flesh.

After a unit with this obsession finishes a charge move, for each model in that unit you can select one enemy unit within 1" of that model and roll one D6; on a 5+ that enemy unit suffers 1 mortal wound.

Dark Technomancers

The products of this Coven are highly sought after, their baleful technologies drawing upon the more unstable and destructive energies of the galaxy. Haemonculi care little if such weapons kill their intended target, or the wielder.

When a unit with this obsession fires Overwatch or is chosen to shoot with, you can choose to enhance any or all of the ranged weapons models in that unit are equipped with. If you do, until the end of the phase, when resolving an attack made with that weapon, add 1 to the wound roll and add 1 to the Damage characteristic of that weapon for that attack. If any unmodified wound rolls of 1 are made for attacks with an enhanced weapon, the firing model suffers 1 mortal wound after shooting with that weapon.

Experimental Creations

Some Haemonculi delight in experimenting on their followers. These monstrous test subjects are intravenously fed a variety of strength-enhancing concoctions, tearing into the enemy to the delight of their master.

Add 1 to the Strength characteristic of all models with this obsession. When resolving an attack made with a poisoned weapon by a model with this obsession against a unit that has a lower Toughness characteristic than the attacking model, add 1 to the wound roll. For the purposes of this obsession, a poisoned weapon is any weapon with the Poisoned Weapon ability (see *Codex: Drukhari*).

Hungry for Flesh

The Haemonculi of this Coven are consumed with the need to sate their appetite for fresh flesh – either to gorge themselves upon it or to experiment upon it, according to each individual's whims.

When a charge roll is made for a unit with this obsession, add 1 to the result.

Masters of Mutagens

Fascination with the fragility of their foes genetic structures drives this Coven. Crafting horrific poisons, the Haemonculi put these to spectacular use on the battlefield, the most innocuous wound leading to rapid and explosive mutation.

When resolving an attack made with a poisoned weapon by a model with this obsession against a unit that is not a **Vehicle** or **Titanic**, an unmodified hit roll of 6 automatically scores a hit and successfully wounds the target (do not make a wound roll). This does not apply to Artefacts of Cruelty. For the purposes of this obsession, a poisoned weapon is any weapon with the Poisoned Weapon ability (see *Codex: Drukhari*).

Master Torturers

The flensing caress and needle-fingered grip of these sadistic monsters finds every pain receptor and hidden weakness of their luckless victims.

When the Torturer's Craft Stratagem (see *Codex: Drukhari*) is used on a unit with this obsession, it only costs 1 Command Point instead of 2.

Obsessive Collectors

The members of this Coven compulsively collect samples of all the many races of the galaxy. Their followers absorb fluids and other substances from their defeated foes, invigorating their own ravaged forms.

When an enemy model is destroyed as a result of an attack made with a melee weapon by a model in a unit from your army with this obsession, you can select one model in that unit to regain up to D3 lost wounds. If the attacking model is a Wrack, you can instead return up to D3 destroyed models to that unit, placing them on the battlefield and in unit coherency (if the models cannot be placed in this way, they are not returned to the battlefield).

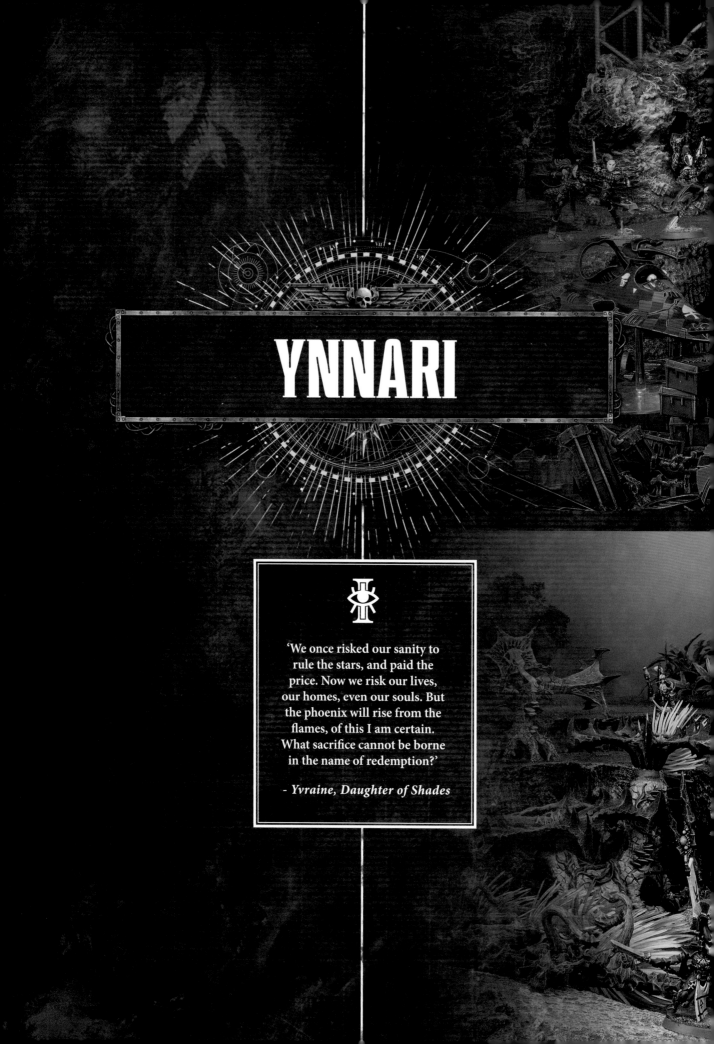

YNNARI

'We once risked our sanity to rule the stars, and paid the price. Now we risk our lives, our homes, even our souls. But the phoenix will rise from the flames, of this I am certain. What sacrifice cannot be borne in the name of redemption?'

- *Yvraine, Daughter of Shades*

CHILDREN OF YNNEAD

In this section you'll find rules for using an Ynnari army in your games of Warhammer 40,000. As well as datasheets for the unique Ynnari characters, you will find Warlord Traits, psychic powers and rules for Battle-forged armies that include YNNARI Detachments – that is, any Detachment that includes only YNNARI units. These rules include the abilities below and a series of Stratagems, Relics and Tactical Objectives. Together, these rules reflect the character and fighting style of the Reborn.

USING AN YNNARI ARMY IN WARHAMMER 40,000

The rules presented in this section are intended to be used in addition to those presented in *Codex: Craftworlds*, *Codex: Drukhari* and *Codex: Harlequins*.

If your army is Battle-forged, you can include Yvraine (pg 69), the Visarch (pg 71) or the Yncarne (pg 73) in any Craftworlds, HARLEQUINS or DRUKHARI Detachment (as defined in their respective codexes), provided that the Detachment does not include any of the following units: any AELDARI named character (other than Yvraine, the Visarch or the Yncarne), any Mandrakes, the Avatar of Khaine, Solitaires or any <HAEMONCULUS COVEN> units. Yvraine, the Visarch and/or the Yncarne can be included in such a Detachment even if a rule (e.g. the Battle Brothers matched play rule) states that every unit in the Detachment must be from the same faction and that faction cannot be AELDARI.

If Yvraine, the Visarch or the Yncarne is included in a Craftworlds, HARLEQUINS or DRUKHARI Detachment, you can choose for that Detachment to either remain a Craftworlds, HARLEQUINS or DRUKHARI Detachment, or for that Detachment to become an YNNARI Detachment.

If you choose for the Detachment to remain a Craftworlds, HARLEQUINS or DRUKHARI Detachment, then Yvraine, the Visarch and/or the Yncarne can be included in that Detachment without preventing other units from gaining the following Detachment abilities: The Path of War, Craftworld Attributes, Vanguard of the Dark City, Raiding Force, Drukhari Obsessions, Defenders of the Black Library, Masque Forms. Note that Yvraine, the Visarch and the Yncarne do not benefit from any of these abilities themselves.

If you choose for the Detachment to become an YNNARI Detachment, then units in that Detachment gain the YNNARI keyword (note that this is not a Faction keyword). The Detachment is no longer considered to be a Craftworlds, HARLEQUINS or DRUKHARI Detachment, and so cannot use their respective Detachment abilities, Stratagems, Warlord Traits, Relics,

psychic powers or Tactical Objectives. Also note that you cannot use Craftworlds, Harlequins and Drukhari Stratagems or psychic powers to affect YNNARI units from your army, even though they may have the appropriate keyword (you cannot use a Craftworlds Stratagem to affect an ASURYANI unit from your army that has the YNNARI keyword, you cannot use a psychic power to affect a friendly ASURYANI unit that has the YNNARI keyword etc.). In addition, replace every instance of <CRAFTWORLD>, <KABAL>, <WYCH CULT> or <MASQUE> on the datasheets of YNNARI units with the appropriate keyword from the table below.

KEYWORD	REPLACE WITH:
<CRAFTWORLD>	REBORN ASURYANI
<KABAL>	REBORN DRUKHARI
<WYCH CULT>	REBORN DRUKHARI
<MASQUE>	REBORN HARLEQUIN

PSYKERS OF THE REBORN

Instead of knowing powers from the Runes of Battle, Runes of Fate or Phantasmancy discipline, YNNARI PSYKERS must know their powers from the Revenant discipline (pg 77).

ABILITIES

If your army is Battle-forged, all Troops units in YNNARI Detachments gain the Reclaim the Galaxy ability. In addition, if your army is Battle-forged, all YNNARI units (other than BEASTS, INCUBI and SCOURGE units) in YNNARI Detachments gain the Strength From Death ability.

RECLAIM THE GALAXY

The Ynnari seek out places or relics of great power in the galaxy as a means to restore the power of the Aeldari, zealously driving off any who would seek to claim these in their place.

A unit with this ability that is within range of an objective marker controls it even if there are more enemy models within range of it. If an enemy unit within range of the objective marker has a similar ability, then it is controlled by the player who has the most models within range as normal.

STRENGTH FROM DEATH

To the Ynnari, the life forces released by the newly dead are invigorating in the extreme, the souls of the fallen spurring a burst of activity.

When a unit is destroyed, units from your army with this ability draw strength from death until the end of the turn.

If a unit is drawing strength from death, that unit fights first in the Fight phase, even if it did not charge. If the enemy has units that have charged, or that have an ability that allows them to fight first in the Fight phase, then alternate choosing units to fight with, starting with the player whose turn is taking place.

When resolving an attack made with a melee weapon by a model that is drawing strength from death, and that made a charge move this turn or has another ability that allows it to fight first in the Fight phase, add 1 to the hit roll.

POINTS VALUES

If you are playing a matched play game, or a game that uses a points limit, you can use the following list to determine the total points cost of your army. Simply add together the points of all your models to determine your army's total points value.

UNITS		
UNIT	MODELS PER UNIT	POINTS PER MODEL (Including wargear)
The Visarch	1	80
The Yncarne	1	280
Yvraine	1	115

YVRAINE

THE DAUGHTER OF SHADES, HIGH PRIESTESS OF THE WHISPERING GOD

The high priestess of Ynnead, the nascent God of the Dead, Yvraine wields her arcane Cronesword with acrobatic grace and brings low her enemies with formidable and terrifying psychic powers. She is a divisive figure in Aeldari society, for her arts border on the necromantic, and her methods are extreme.

Soon after Ynnead was first roused from slumbering potentiality, a fraction of his will and power was imparted to a single soul – Yvraine, the Daughter of Shades. Chosen by fate, she was in spirit the closest living thing to the ancient Aeldari who had existed before Slaanesh erupted into being. An exile from Biel-Tan after following the Paths of the Warrior and the Witch, Yvraine had roamed to every corner of Aeldari society. She had become an outcast, then a Corsair commander. Finally, after a costly mutiny, she fell from grace entirely to become an exile. Stripped of her grandeur, humbled by those who once called her mistress, Yvraine eked out a new existence within the haunted streets of Commorragh. She fought tooth and nail to become part of the Wych Cults, and eventually succeeded through talent as much as treachery. Such was her skill as a warrior that she rose to the rank of Succubus. It was in the white-

hot crucible of arena conflict that Yvraine crossed the threshold of death, and found herself infused with the energies of Ynnead. That crux point of fate saw the birth of a new creed – in one mind-blasting moment Yvraine became a conduit for deathly power, invested with the ability to manipulate spirit energy and pass on her esoteric skills to those who joined her macabre religion.

Yvraine cut her way free from the daemonic infestation that rocked Commorragh soon after ascension. She made her way back to the craftworld of her birth, Biel-Tan – and in the process, set in motion the events that saw the world-ship fractured into skeletal shards of its former glory. The shattering of Biel-Tan's infinity circuit caused a vast explosion of psychic energies that caused warp vortices to spiral into being around the stricken craftworld, but also gave a focal

point for the God of the Dead to manifest his avatar in realspace.

A great many Aeldari have joined Yvraine's cause, including Asuryani, Drukhari, Harlequins and even a strange psychic familiar known as a Gyrinx. The effects of their new deity Ynnead can be seen manifesting around them. Yvraine's Reborn can draw upon the souls within the spirit stones they wear to bolster their own abilities, siphon the power of those slain nearby to invigorate their attacks, and turn their foes to ashes and dust with the strange weapons and psychic powers they wield. They have learned the secrets of the dead, bringing them closer to their ancestors and the lost glories of their fallen race. However, many see Yvraine and her Ynnari as corrupted by the very daemonic forces she seeks to thwart, whilst others believe she is already dead inside. And perhaps they are right.

YVRAINE

6 POWER

NAME	M	WS	BS	S	T	W	A	Ld	Sv
Yvraine	8"	2+	2+	3	3	5	4	9	6+

Yvraine is a single model equipped with: Kha-vir, the Sword of Sorrows. You can only include one of this model in your army.

WEAPON	RANGE	TYPE	S	AP	D	ABILITIES
Kha-vir, the Sword of Sorrows	Melee	Melee	+1	-2	D3	-

ABILITIES	**Strength From Death** (pg 67)	**Runesuit:** This model has a 4+ invulnerable save.
	Herald of Ynnead: When another **AELDARI** model is slain within 6" of this model, you can roll one D6; on a 4+ this model regains 1 lost wound. If that model was a **PSYKER**, you can immediately generate one additional psychic power for this model to know from the Revenant discipline.	**Gyrinx Familiar:** When a Psychic test or Deny the Witch test is taken for this model, add 1 to the result. **Revered Figurehead:** This model can embark aboard any **AELDARI TRANSPORT** model, regardless of that model's transport restrictions.

PSYKER	This model can attempt to manifest two psychic powers in your Psychic phase and attempt to deny one psychic power in your opponent's Psychic phase. It knows *Smite* and two psychic powers from the Revenant discipline (pg 77).
FACTION KEYWORDS	**AELDARI, YNNARI**
KEYWORDS	**CHARACTER, INFANTRY, PSYKER, YVRAINE**

Amongst ancient Aeldari ruins, Yvraine seeks out lost treasures of her race, closely guarded by a squad of Reborn Dire Avengers.

THE VISARCH

BLADE OF YNNEAD

The Visarch strides into the fray with the surety of a master swordsman. In him is an echo of the Aeldari at the height of their power. Acting as Yvraine's escort, teacher and confidante, he is a lynchpin in the Ynnari inner circle. Any who would harm his mistress must first meet him blade to blade – no enviable task.

The Visarch is Yvraine's chosen champion. He epitomises the matchless grace of the Aeldari in form as well as deed. Clad in baroque armour of the ancient Bel-Anshoc style, the Visarch wears many faces upon his battle plate, just as he channels many souls within his mortal form. Where one personality's skills are not suited to his immediate need, another rises to the fore, lending him a critical edge. The Visarch can strike with the sure sword of an Exarch, channel the lethal ruthlessness of an Incubus, or use the acrobatic prowess of a Wych, darting through the enemy lines to leave only twitching limbs and dismembered torsos in his wake. Those who scream in pain soon find themselves robbed of their voices, for the Sword of Silent Screams brings a deathly hush when drawn in anger – the silence of the grave.

The Visarch is the first of the Aeldari to harness the power of a Cronesword. He was once known as Exarch Laarian, but since encountering the Daughter of Shades, he has become something stranger and more unsettling than one of Khaine's shrinekeepers. Once an Exarch of considerable standing upon Biel-Tan, the Visarch had taught Yvraine in her former life as an Aspect Warrior. Seeing much potential in her acrobatic skills, he been greatly saddened when she had left his shrine. He could barely accept that she had forsaken the way of the Dire Avenger in favour of the Witch Path, but when she then chose the way of the Outcast, and eventually a life of murder and moral decrepitude in Commorragh, his spirit broke. Though he would not admit it to himself, the depths of his feelings for Yvraine diverted his course.

In a nigh-unprecedented decision, the Visarch left his shrine in the hands of his foremost disciples, breaking the faith of the Exarch tradition to follow Yvraine along the dark thread of fate she had made for herself. Posing as an Incubus, he fought his way to a position of prominence in the Dark City, the better to keep watch over his ward. In the grand shrine of the Coiled Blade, he joined those accomplished killers sometimes called the Scarlet Incubi by those afraid to name them. Laarian struck down the Klaivex after a gruelling duel and took the role as right of conquest. Perhaps it was this act that saw him embody the ancient Aeldari more than most. Perhaps it was his ceaseless study of the arts of death that drew him close to Ynnead. Perhaps it was fate alone. From that moment on, however, Laarian found a deep and spiritual connection with the Whispering God. He has served him ever since – and in doing so, has been drawn to Yvraine's side once more.

THE VISARCH

NAME	M	WS	BS	S	T	W	A	Ld	Sv
The Visarch	8"	2+	2+	3	3	5	5	9	3+

The Visarch is a single model equipped with: Asu-var, the Sword of Silent Screams. He has a forceshield. You can only include one of this model in your army.

WEAPON	RANGE	TYPE	S	AP	D	ABILITIES
Asu-var, the Sword of Silent Screams	Melee	Melee	+2	-3	D3	If any models in a unit are destroyed as a result of an attack made with this weapon in a turn, subtract 1 from the Leadership characteristic of that unit until the end of that turn.

ABILITIES	
Strength From Death (pg 67) **Champion of Ynnead:** When another **Aeldari** model is slain within 6" of this model, you can roll one D6; on a 4+ this model regains 1 lost wound. If that model was a **Character**, add 1 to this model's Attacks characteristic. **Way of the Blade:** Re-roll hit rolls of 1 for attacks made with melee weapons by friendly **Ynnari** models whilst their unit is within 6" of this model.	**Warden of Yvraine:** When a friendly **Yvraine** model within 3" of this model would lose any wounds as a result of an attack made against that model, this model can attempt to intercept that attack. Roll one D6; on a 2+ that model does not lose those wounds and this unit suffers 1 mortal wound for each of those wounds. **Forceshield:** This model has a 4+ invulnerable save. **Revered Figurehead:** This model can embark aboard any **Aeldari Transport** model, regardless of that model's transport restrictions.

FACTION KEYWORDS	**Aeldari, Ynnari**
KEYWORDS	**Character, Infantry, The Visarch**

A swordsman of sublime skill, the Visarch fights unwaveringly for Yvraine and Ynnead, determined to secure his race's future.

THE YNCARNE
DEATHLY AVATAR OF YNNEAD

The Yncarne is a being both beautiful and terrible, whose mastery over deathly energies is born from the supernatural powers of Ynnead himself. It does not enter the fray as a mortal might, but bursts screaming from the ground wherever the energies of death are strongest. Those Ynnari around it are filled with unnatural vigour.

The Yncarne is eerily beautiful and extremely unsettling at the same time, a manifestation of morbid energies that communicates only through death and the manipulation of spiritual energy. It is thought of by many as the Avatar of Ynnead, much in the way that the Bloody-Handed God has its own incarnations on the mortal plane. The comparison is valid, yet also flawed, for there is but one Yncarne – Ynnead's power waxes with each new death, true enough, but he has but a fraction of his potential realised in realspace. Furthermore, the coalescence of this chimeric figure was a direct result of the fracture of Biel-Tan and the immense psychic trauma that triggered it – a trauma triggered by daemonic intrusion. Some of the Reborn's detractors have been bold enough to claim that the Yncarne, far from being the nemesis of Slaanesh in physical form, is in actuality polluted by the very forces it was intended to bring low.

With a hideous tearing sound, the corpse-strewn battleground cracks and glows white, a towering form bursting from the blood-soaked earth amongst an ectoplasmic storm. The Yncarne has come, bane of the lesser races and icon of rebirth for the mighty Aeldari. This incarnation of morbid energies drifts towards its prey amongst a vortex of deathly whispers, a roaring psychic hurricane ripping the life from those who earn its ire. Mortal foes find their doom closing in, as unstoppable as the night. Those not turned to dust at the Yncarne's gaze or sent tumbling to the ground as soulless husks are sliced in two by the Sword of Souls, a quicksilver blade that can change shape at need. Those Ynnari who fight alongside this creature are invigorated by a cold and chilling power, lent the icy determination of the Reborn.

THE YNCARNE

NAME	M	WS	BS	S	T	W	A	Ld	Sv
The Yncarne	8"	2+	2+	6	6	9	6	9	3+

The Yncarne is a single model equipped with: Vilith-zhar, the Sword of Souls. You can only include one of this model in your army.

WEAPON	RANGE	TYPE	S	AP	D	ABILITIES
Vilith-zhar, the Sword of Souls	Melee	Melee	User	-4	D6	When resolving an attack made with this weapon, you can re-roll the wound roll.

ABILITIES	
Strength From Death (pg 67) **Daemonic Avatar:** This model has a 4+ invulnerable save. **Inevitable Death:** When you set up this model, it can be set up in waiting rather than on the battlefield. If it is, then when another unit is destroyed, after removing the last model in that unit from play, you can set up this model as close as possible to the previous position of that model, more than 1" away from any enemy models. This model cannot charge in a turn in which it was set up in this manner. **Blessings of the Whispering God:** When a friendly YNNARI unit within 6" of this model would lose a wound, roll one D6; on a 6 that wound is not lost.	**Summoned by Death:** When another unit is destroyed, after removing the last model in that unit from play, you can remove this model from the battlefield and can set it up as close as possible to the previous position of that model, more than 1" away from any enemy models. This model cannot charge in a turn in which it was set up in this manner. **Ynnead Stirs:** When a Morale test is taken for a friendly YNNARI unit within 6" of this model, do not roll the dice; it is automatically passed. **Avatar of Ynnead:** When another AELDARI model is destroyed within 6" of this model, you can roll one D6; on a 4+ this model regains 1 lost wound.

PSYKER	This model can attempt to manifest two psychic powers in your Psychic phase and attempt to deny one psychic power in your opponent's Psychic phase. It knows *Smite* and two psychic powers from the Revenant discipline (pg 77).
FACTION KEYWORDS	AELDARI, YNNARI
KEYWORDS	CHARACTER, MONSTER, DAEMON, FLY, PSYKER, THE YNCARNE

Emerging from a wraithbone webway gate, the triumvirate of Ynnead stride to war.

YNNARI STRATAGEMS

If your army is Battle-forged and includes any YNNARI Detachments (excluding Auxiliary Support Detachments), you have access to the Stratagems shown here, meaning you can spend Command Points to activate them. These help to reflect the unique strategies used by the Reborn on the battlefield. If a Stratagem is used before the battle to upgrade a unit (e.g. Exalted of Ynnead) and you have an army roster, you must note on it which Stratagems are used to upgrade which units.

A TASTE FOR DEATH
1CP

Ynnari Stratagem

When one of the Reborn sees the soul-stuff of the foe leaving its body, they feel a renewed sense of purpose.

Use this Stratagem in the Shooting or Charge phase, when an enemy unit is destroyed as a result of an attack made with a ranged weapon by an YNNARI model from your army. Until the end of the turn, when resolving an attack made with a melee weapon by a model in that model's unit, add 1 to the hit roll.

INEVITABLE FATE
2CP

Ynnari Stratagem

The Ynnari know that all life must end in order to be reborn, and hasten to bring their enemy closer to that demise as quickly as possible.

Use this Stratagem at the start of the Fight phase. Select one enemy unit. Until the end of that phase, when resolving an attack made with a melee weapon by an YNNARI unit from your army against that unit, you can re-roll the wound roll.

WHISPERING SPIRITS
2CP

Ynnari Stratagem

The Ynnari are surrounded by the souls of the dead, whose sibilant whispers distract and unnerve nearby foes.

Use this Stratagem in the Morale phase, before a Morale test is taken for an enemy unit within 1" of any YNNARI units from your army. Until the end of the phase, subtract 2 from that enemy unit's Leadership characteristic.

ACOLYTE OF YNNEAD
1CP

Ynnari Stratagem

Those psykers amongst the Ynnari hosts can use the souls of the recently dead to focus their powers.

Use this Stratagem before an YNNARI PSYKER model from your army attempts to manifest a psychic power from the Revenant discipline. Add 3 to the total for that Psychic test if any enemy units were destroyed this phase.

YNNEAD'S NET
2CP

Ynnari Stratagem

As the warhost closes upon the foe, jetbike-mounted riders swoop to trap the enemy.

Use this Stratagem at the start of your Charge phase. Select one YNNARI BIKER unit from your army. That unit can charge even if it Advanced this turn.

REBORN TOGETHER
1CP

Ynnari Stratagem

The goal of the Ynnari is to save every member of the Aeldari race, whatever their previous allegiance.

Use this Stratagem at the start of the Morale phase. Until the end of that phase, add 2 to the Leadership characteristic of YNNARI units from your army whilst they are within 6" of any other friendly YNNARI units.

UNITED IN DEATH
2CP

Ynnari Stratagem

When the Ynnari act as one, their blows fall like rain, the storm of blades in the name of the God of the Dead.

Use this Stratagem at the start of the Fight phase. Select one REBORN ASURYANI, one REBORN HARLEQUINS and one REBORN DRUKHARI unit from your army. Until the end of that phase, add 1 to the Attacks characteristic of models in those units whilst they are drawing strength from death.

SHRINE OF THE WHISPERING GOD
1CP

Ynnari Stratagem

Though rare, it is not completely unheard of for Incubi to become true devotees of Ynnead. Most famous are the Incubi of the Coiled Blade, who have fought beside the Visarch on countless battlefields.

Use this Stratagem before the battle. Select up to three YNNARI INCUBI units from your army. Those units gain the Strength From Death ability.

ARTEFACTS OF DEATH
1CP

Ynnari Stratagem

When the Ynnari gather in a great host, the presence of so many relics of great power means victory is assured.

Use this Stratagem before the battle. Your army can have one additional Relic of Ynnead. All of the Relics your army includes must be different and be given to different models.

THE GREAT ENEMY
1CP

Ynnari Stratagem

The Aeldari reserve a ferocious loathing for Slaanesh and its followers.

Use this Stratagem in the Fight phase, when an **YNNARI** unit from your army is chosen to fight with. Until the end of that phase, when resolving an attack made by a model in that unit against a **SLAANESH** unit, you can re-roll the wound roll.

WEBWAY AMBUSH
1/3CP

Ynnari Stratagem

With the spirits of the dead guiding their every step, the Reborn can navigate the webway with ease.

Use this Stratagem during deployment. If you spend 1 CP, you can set up one **YNNARI INFANTRY**, **YNNARI BIKER** or **YNNARI BEAST** unit from your army in the webway instead of placing it on the battlefield. If you spend 3 CPs, you can set up two such units in the webway instead. A unit in the webway can emerge at the end of any of your Movement phases – set it up anywhere on the battlefield that is more than 9" away from any enemy models. This Stratagem can only be used once per battle

FIRE AND FADE
1CP

Ynnari Stratagem

The Aeldari are masters at using hit and run tactics, striking a killing blow before withdrawing from reprisal.

You can use this Stratagem in your Shooting phase, after an **YNNARI** unit from your army shoots. That unit can move up to 7" as if it were your Movement phase, but it cannot Advance as part of that move and cannot charge this turn.

DEADLY MISDIRECTION
2CP

Ynnari Stratagem

With the Aeldari, nothing is what it seems. What appears to be a victory can soon transform into a defeat.

Use this Stratagem in your Movement phase, when an **YNNARI** unit from your army Falls Back. That unit can still shoot and charge this turn

EXALTED OF YNNEAD
1CP

Ynnari Stratagem

The hope presented by the Reborn draws in even the mightiest heroes of the Aeldari.

Use this Stratagem before the battle, after nominating your Warlord. Select one Ynnari **CHARACTER** model from your army that is not your Warlord and generate one Warlord Trait for it; it is regarded as your Warlord for the purposes of that Warlord Trait. Each Warlord Trait in your army must be unique (if randomly generated, re-roll duplicate results). You can only use this Stratagem once per battle.

SOULS OF THE STRONGEST
1CP

Ynnari Stratagem

Those souls in the galaxy that burn strong and bright can be harnessed to great effect by Ynnead's followers.

Use this Stratagem in any phase, when your opponent's Warlord is destroyed. Until the end of the battle, units from your army with the Strength From Death ability draw strength from death, even if a unit has not been destroyed in a turn.

BACK FROM THE BRINK
2CP

Ynnari Stratagem

Those infused with death are not easy to slay.

Use this Stratagem in any phase, when an **YNNARI INFANTRY CHARACTER** or **YNNARI BIKER CHARACTER** model from your army is destroyed. Roll one D6; on a 4+ return that model to play with D3 wounds remaining, placing it as close as possible to its previous position and more than 1" away from any enemy models. This Stratagem cannot be used on the same model more than once per battle.

LIGHTNING-FAST REACTIONS
2CP

Ynnari Stratagem

The Aeldari are possessed of preternatural reflexes.

Use this Stratagem in your opponent's Shooting phase or the Fight phase, when an **YNNARI** unit from your army with the **INFANTRY** and/or **FLY** keyword is chosen as the target of an attack. Until the end of that phase, when resolving an attack against that unit, subtract 1 from the hit roll.

WARLORD TRAITS

Amongst the Reborn are found Aeldari from every part of their scattered race. The mightiest of these warriors inevitably rise to command great hosts of the Reborn.

If an **Ynnari Character** model is your Warlord, you can use the Ynnari Warlord Traits table to determine what Warlord Trait they have. You can either roll one D6 to randomly generate one, or you can select one.

D6 WARLORD TRAIT

1 LORD OF REBIRTH

Some Ynnari have mastered the cycle of death and rebirth.

At the start of the battle round, this Warlord regains up to 1 lost wound. When this Warlord would lose a wound, roll one D6; on a 5+ that wound is not lost.

2 WARDEN OF SOULS

This warrior of the Reborn is the keeper of many souls; their mastery over deathly energy is unparalleled.

Whilst this Warlord is drawing strength from death, add 1 to their Attacks and Strength characteristics.

3 WALKER OF MANY PATHS

The hard-earned skills of this follower of Ynnead have been honed by walking the many paths of the Aeldari.

Once per turn, when resolving an attack made by this Warlord, you can re-roll one hit roll or you can re-roll one wound roll. Whilst this Warlord is on the battlefield, you can roll one D6 for each Command Point you spend to use a Stratagem; on a 5+ that Command Point is refunded. You can only have 1 Command Point refunded per battle round by this Warlord Trait.

4 FEAR OF THE GRAVE

Ynnead knows neither mercy nor fear – the same cannot be said of the god's foes.

Subtract 1 from the Leadership characteristic of models in enemy units whilst their unit is within 6" of this Warlord; subtract 2 instead if any enemy units have been destroyed as a result of an attack made by this Warlord this turn.

5 FAVOURED OF YNNEAD

The energies of the dead seek this Aeldari out, swirling around them like a gale and carrying them into the foe.

When this Warlord piles in or consolidates, they can move up to 6" instead of up to 3".

6 MASTER OF DEATH

This champion of the Reborn has great expertise in severing the cord that binds the body to the soul.

When resolving an attack made with a melee weapon by this Warlord, an unmodified hit roll of 6 scores 1 additional hit.

NAMED CHARACTERS AND WARLORD TRAITS

If one of the following characters is your Warlord, they must have the associated Warlord Trait shown below:

CHARACTER	WARLORD TRAIT
Yvraine	Warden of Souls
Visarch	Master of Death
Yncarne	Fear of the Grave

'To the dark side of the Aeldari mind, all life is to be expended on a whim. Cruelty and generosity are but the impulse of a moment. Beauty and sensuality are virtues that can be expressed in bloodshed just as easily as in song. To an unfettered Aeldari mind there is neither sanity nor madness, but merely a wave of perfect existence fulfilled by its own savage momentum.'

- Ralamine Mung,
Ordo Xenos

REVENANT DISCIPLINE

Amongst the Reborn, even those psykers who have honed their powers for centuries will find their abilities augmented by the god of death.

Before the battle, generate the psychic powers for **YNNARI PSYKER** models that know powers from the Revenant discipline using the table below. You can either roll one D6 to generate each power randomly (re-rolling duplicate results), or you can select which powers the psyker knows.

D6 PSYCHIC POWER

1 GAZE OF YNNEAD

The psyker's eyes blaze with fire as they channel the power of Ynnead.

Gaze of Ynnead has a warp charge value of 6. If manifested, select one enemy unit that is within 18" of and visible to this psyker and roll one D6: on a 1, that unit suffers 1 mortal wound; on a 2-5 that unit suffers D3 mortal wounds; on a 6, that unit suffers D6 mortal wounds.

2 STORM OF WHISPERS

The psyker's voice joins with those of the dead to drive the foe insane.

Storm of Whispers has a warp charge value of 6. If manifested, roll three D6 for each enemy unit within 6" of this psyker; for each result of 6, the unit being rolled for suffers 1 mortal wound.

3 WORD OF THE PHOENIX

The psyker calls upon the rebirthing energies of the mythical phoenix.

Word of the Phoenix has a warp charge value of 5. If manifested, select one friendly **YNNARI INFANTRY** or **YNNARI BIKER** unit within 18" of this psyker. If that unit contains a model that has lost any wounds, that model regains up to D3 lost wounds. Otherwise, if any models from that unit have been destroyed, roll one D6; on a 4+ you can return one destroyed model from that unit to the battlefield with 1 wound remaining, placing it in unit coherency (if the model

cannot be placed in this way, it is not returned to the battlefield).

4 UNBIND SOULS

The psyker reaches out with their powers to weaken the bond between soul and body.

Unbind Souls has a warp charge value of 6. If manifested, select one enemy unit within 18" of this psyker. Until the start of your next Psychic phase, when resolving an attack made with a melee weapon by a friendly **YNNARI** model against that enemy unit, you can re-roll the wound roll.

5 SHIELD OF YNNEAD

The psyker manifests a shield of spiritual energy around their allies.

Shield of Ynnead has a warp charge value of 7. If manifested, until the start of your next Psychic phase, friendly **YNNARI** units have a 5+ invulnerable save whilst they are within 6" of this psyker.

6 ANCESTOR'S GRACE

Drawing upon the greatness that is the genetic legacy of all Aeldari, the psyker bolsters their fellows.

Ancestor's Grace has a warp charge value of 5. If manifested, select one friendly **YNNARI** unit within 18" of this psyker. Until the start of your next Psychic phase, when resolving an attack made by a model in that unit, re-roll a hit roll of 1.

'They seek to give rise to the god of death, these Ynnari, and in doing so become the masters of all mortality. Are the lessons of the aeons so easily cast aside?'

- Autarch Relethere of Alaitoc

RELICS OF YNNEAD

With Asuryani, Drukhari and Harlequins amongst its numbers, the Reborn bring to battle mighty artefacts from across the scattered Aeldari race. From ancient treasures to items crafted to manipulate the energies of death, all of these relics are potent tools for furthering the will of Ynnead.

If your army is led by an **Ynnari** Warlord, you can give one of the following Relics of Ynnead to an **Ynnari Character** model from your army. Named characters and **Vehicle** models cannot be given any of the following Relics.

Note that some Relics are weapons that replace one of the model's existing weapons. Where this is the case, you must, if you are using points values, still pay the cost of the weapon that is being replaced. Write down any Relics your models have on your army roster.

HUNGERING BLADE

Within the Hungering Blade is a terrible appetite, a longing to turn all living Aeldari to inert corpses in order to see the supremacy of Ynnead hastened and She Who Thirsts defeated. Great care must be taken by the wielder, for the slightest scratch upon the flesh from this glistening blade can result in a deadly necrosis that turns the body to dust in the space of a few seconds. Its effects upon non-Aeldari life forms are just as profound.

Model equipped with a power sword, star glaive or husk blade only. This Relic replaces a power sword, star glaive or husk blade and has the following profile:

WEAPON	RANGE	TYPE	S	AP	D
Hungering Blade	Melee	Melee	+3	-3	2
Abilities: When resolving an attack made with this weapon, an unmodified wound roll of 6 inflicts 1 mortal wound on the target in addition to any other damage.					

SONG OF YNNEAD

The hiss of the monomolecular discs that shoot from this pistol rises to a deafening roar of triumph when it claims a life. Those nearby are assailed by terrible hallucinations as vengeful spirits clamour within their minds.

Model equipped with a shuriken pistol only. This Relic replaces a shuriken pistol and has the following profile:

WEAPON	RANGE	TYPE	S	AP	D
Song of Ynnead	18"	Pistol 3	5	-1	1
Abilities: When resolving an attack made with this weapon, on a wound roll of 6+ this weapon has an Armour Penetration characteristic of -3 for that attack. If any models in a unit are destroyed as a result of an attack made with this weapon in a turn, subtract 1 from the Leadership characteristic of that unit until the end of that turn.					

MIRRORGAZE

This helm is covered in mosaic shards from the famed Crystal Mirror. Its facets can channel the blinding light of battle to rob the sight of those who look upon it, giving the wearer a crucial moment of advantage.

When resolving an attack made against a model with this Relic, subtract 1 from the hit roll.

SOULSNARE

This rune-inscribed orb is filled with the psychic gossamer of Ynnead's all-constraining net. When hurled at the ground, it bursts open in a cloud of glittering thread that cuts through those standing nearby, reducing their bodies to lifeless clay as their spirits howl in anguish.

Once per game, when a model with this Relic is chosen to shoot with in your Shooting phase, that model can throw the Soulsnare instead of shooting with any ranged weapons it is equipped with. Select one enemy unit within 6" of and visible to that model, and roll one D6: on a 2-5, that enemy unit suffers D3 mortal wounds, and that model regains up to a number of wounds equal to the number of wounds lost by that unit; on a 6, that enemy unit suffers D6 mortal wounds and that model regains any lost wounds.

THE LOST SHROUD

This cloak was woven from the ectoplasmic by-product that wisped from Craftworld Biel-Tan's ravaged infinity circuit after the Daemon invasion that saw it sundered. Although its daemonic ties cause it to be regarded as dangerous in the extreme, within its shimmering weave the deathless blessing of Ynnead is exceedingly powerful.

When resolving an attack made against a model with this Relic, halve any damage inflicted (rounding up). When a model with this Relic would lose a wound, roll one D6; on a 5+ that wound is not lost.

CORAG HAI'S LOCKET

The ancient priestess Corag Hai died spectacularly when Ynnead chose his emissary to the living Aeldari world. Only this soulsteel trinket was left amongst the dust of her discorporation. The bearer can channel the energies of rebirth whenever they are near the fires of a slain victim.

When an enemy unit is destroyed as a result of an attack made by a model with this Relic, add 1 to that model's Move and Attacks characteristics.

TACTICAL OBJECTIVES

The Ynnari use all the powers at their disposal to hasten the death of their foe and bring about the salvation of their race. For them, there are no barriers on the road to victory.

If your army is led by an **YNNARI** Warlord, these Tactical Objectives replace the Capture and Control Tactical Objectives (numbers 11-16) in the *Warhammer 40,000* rulebook. If a mission uses Tactical Objectives, players use the normal rules for using Tactical Objectives with the following exception: when an Ynnari player generates a Capture and Control objective (numbers 11-16), they instead generate the corresponding Ynnari Tactical Objective, as shown below. Other Tactical Objectives (numbers 21-66) are generated normally.

D66	TACTICAL OBJECTIVE
11	Spirit Sanctuary
12	Harness the Spirits
13	For Ynnead's Glory
14	Surety of Purpose
15	Death's Every Visage
16	Soulsurge

11 SPIRIT SANCTUARY

Some mystical locales provide a rich source of life force, havens for lost souls and reservoirs of power for the Reborn.

When this Tactical Objective is generated, roll one D6. Score 1 victory point if no enemy units are controlling the objective marker corresponding to the result rolled at the end of this turn.

Ynnari

14 SURETY OF PURPOSE

There is no Aeldari soul that does not draw strength from a bold strategy well-executed. Let the lesser races look on in awe!

Score D3 victory points if you have achieved at least two other Tactical Objectives this turn.

Ynnari

12 HARNESS THE SPIRITS

Use the energies of the dead to channel your will, and the spirits will gladly lend their ethereal powers to your cause.

Score 1 victory point if at least one **YNNARI** model from your army successfully manifested a psychic power from the Revenant discipline this turn.

Ynnari

15 DEATH'S EVERY VISAGE

The Whispering God has a million faces – show the enemy your mastery over each and every form of death.

Score 1 victory point if at least one enemy unit was destroyed in either the Psychic, Shooting or Fight phase of this turn as a result of a Psychic power manifested or attack made by an **YNNARI** model from your army. Score D3 victory points instead if at least one enemy unit was destroyed in all three of these phases.

Ynnari

13 FOR YNNEAD'S GLORY

For the Ynnari, every death is a wellspring of potential waiting to be harnessed.

Score 1 victory point if three or more units were destroyed during this turn as a result of attacks made by **YNNARI** units from your army.

Ynnari

16 SOULSURGE

Bringing death to the denizens of the living realm increases the glory and power of Ynnead. Let the shadow of death empower you!

Score 1 victory point if three or more units were destroyed during this turn as a result of attacks made by **YNNARI** units from your army whilst those **YNNARI** units were drawing strength from death.

Ynnari

Upon the world of Iathglas, at the heart of a blood-spattered clearing near the planet's shimmering world-shrine, a daemonic hunter battled the Daughter of Shades and her chosen champions. War raged all around them. Everywhere the Aeldari fought as one against the Daemons of Slaanesh and the duel in the clearing took place as though at the heart of a violent storm. Beneath the crimson light of Miaghu they fought, the Daemon's claws and whip-like tendrils engaging all five champions at once. Lelith's deadly knives stabbed up at its face, but were blocked by the creature's shining aegis. Yvraine cut through one tentacle-whip with her Cronesword only to find another of the vile things grappling her wrist.

The Midnight Solitaire stabbed his Harlequin's Kiss between Helbane's exposed ribs, the device hissing as its monomolecular wire unspooled. Helbane merely shivered as if in ecstasy, then snipped the Cegorachi warrior bodily in half. The hilt of the Daemon's deadly longspear came round to catch Jain Zar's midriff as she was mid-leap. The blow should have broken her spine, but the Phoenix Lord channelled the energy of the dying Aeldari beneath her just as Yvraine had taught her. Jain Zar gave vent to a war shout and levelled a spinning slash from her own polearm that cut the Daemon's brow to blind it with its own ichor. Helbane staggered back, shield and pseudopods raised in defence, hissing in outrage.

'Slaanesh's due,' the Daemon spat, and Yvraine heard true disgust in the thing's voice. 'That soul was not yours to take!'

Too late Yvraine realised the weakness was feigned, the angry words a distraction. The Visarch swept his sword in two-handed for a kill strike. Helbane flipped its spear high as it blocked the blow, then deftly caught the Visarch's blade between finger and thumb. It yanked him forwards so the falling spear impaled him from collarbone to shin. At the same time a claw lunged out for Yvraine. She felt a gouging mass of pain in her neck as the grasping pincer tore away half her throat. Blood spurted. She fell, her vision turning black. Helbane's whispered syllables crowded into her mind. The energies of Ynnead were being torn from her by some horrific warp-spell. True death was near. From this, there would be no coming back.

As Yvraine's back touched the ground she felt a great swell of invigorating energy pour into her from the virgin soil beneath. Iathglas' world spirit had need of her still. The Daughter of Shades regained her senses as a great burst of scintillating energy flowed through her, only to see the Visarch's corpse topple into a mound of dead leaves. Where he fell the Yncarne burst from the ground, given terrible animus. It screamed in triumph as it drank in the deathly energies of the corpses strewn around the clearing, then launched itself at Helbane. The giant Daemon-creatures duelled like gods, blades flashing in the red twilight. A blow landed from the Yncarne's great Cronesword. Helbane struck back hard, its spear piercing the Yncarne's chest, but the grinning rictus on the avatar's face merely widened. It clutched the spear like a lover's gift, locking it in place.

Yvraine leapt, her sword slashing the Daemon's midriff even as Jain Zar's gleaming polearm burst from the centre of its chest. A moment later, Lelith's blades found their mark in the creature's eyes. With a piercing shriek, the Daemon shimmered, its form wavering, beginning to dissipate.

'The Daemon is banished!' cried Yvraine, dropping to her knees beside the Visarch and channelling the energies of rebirth to knit his ruptured form. She felt a fierce sense of vindication at the victory of her assembled champions. Surely, she thought, the metaphor of such a combined victory over She Who Thirsts would not be lost upon her kin. From the clearing's edge came shouts of triumph as the surviving Aeldari saw their foes flicker and fade, the hunting party banished along with their leader. There would be sorrow for the losses suffered this day, thought Yvraine, but those who would do Ynnead's will needed to understand that–

Cruel laughter cut across her thoughts. Yvraine's blood turned to ice as she realised the voice was Helbane's. She looked up to see her bloodied champions spinning, raising their blades anew as the daemon's form shuddered back into focus, though it remained ephemeral as the gossamer mists of dawn. Jain Zar struck, yet her blade cut air as if the daemon was not there at all.

'Because you are not truly here, are you?' asked Yvraine, exhaustion and frustration making her voice leaden. Helbane's lips quirked into a cruel and predatory smirk.

'No more than a glamour, quarry-mine,' it purred. 'Solid enough to give good sport, and to test your strength, but only an echo of my true essence.'

'Why?' asked Yvraine, hearing murmurs of dismay spreading through the assembled Aeldari. What, she could hear them asking, had they fought for here? Had they simply been playthings for She Who Thirsts? Yvraine pictured cracks racing through the fragile alliance she had hoped to fashion, and closed her eyes against the frustration that threatened to overwhelm her.

'Yessss, you have your answer do you not, quarry-mine?' whispered Helbane, its voice fading. 'You have won nothing this day but a little more time to flee, terrified, powerless. The tormented soul is always sweeter…'

Yvraine opened her eyes to see the Daemon gone and the Aeldari around her already falling into arguments of recrimination, or shedding sorrowful tears of loss. For herself she tasted only ashes. There would be no unity won this day, and out there, somewhere, the thing still hunted her.

The Visarch placed a hand upon Yvraine's shoulder and she looked into his expressionless mask.

'Come,' he said, voice weak and hoarse from his recent resurrection. 'The Whispering God still has need of us.'

Yvraine nodded and together they turned to leave the clearing, to salvage what they could of this dreadful day. The Ynnari were not defeated yet, thought Yvraine fiercely, and the souls within her clamoured in agreement. Ynnead would still wake and Slaanesh would still fall. This she vowed, no matter the cost.